G000016656

ADAPTED BY PHIL PORTER
BASED ON THE NOVEL BY TIM BOWLER

StarSeeKeR

Heinemann is an imprint of Pearson Education Limited, a company incorporated in England and Wales, having its registered office at Edinburgh Gate, Harlow, Essex, CM20 2JE. Registered company number: 872828

www.heinemann.co.uk

This edition of *Starseeker* © Pearson Education Limited 2008

Starseeker stage adaptation © Phil Porter 2007
Starseeker © Tim Bowler 2002

Introduction by Tim Bowler © Tim Bowler
Introduction by Phil Porter © Phil Porter

This edition of *Starseeker* first published by Heinemann, 2008
Published by arrangement with Oberon Books Ltd

Phil Porter's stage adaptation of *Starseeker* first published by Oberon Books, 2007

12 11 10 09
10 9 8 7 6 5 4 3 2

British Library Cataloguing in Publication Data is available from the British Library on request.

ISBN 978 0435233 43 3

Typeset by Phoenix Photosetting, Chatham Kent
Cover photos © iStockphoto
Printed in China (CTPS/02)

Acknowledgements
Every effort has been made to contact copyright holders of material reproduced in this book. Any omissions will be rectified in subsequent printings if notice is given to the publishers.

Extracts from *Starseeker* by Tim Bowler, published by OUP 2002. Copyright © Tim Bowler 2002. (Extracts are on pages 120, 122–23.)

The authors and publisher would like to thank the following individual for permission to reproduce photographs:

pp191 –194: Robert Day

Contents

Scheme of work and teaching resources
To help deliver the activities on pages 95–141, extensive
teaching materials are available to download free from
www.heinemann.co.uk/literature.

Introduction by Phil Porter

In the autumn of 2006, director Dani Parr asked me to read Tim Bowler's *Starseeker* with a view to adapting it for the stage. I read the book and was struck, first of all, by the character of Luke. His sensitivity to sound and music, and the visions that stem from that gift, seemed so extraordinary. And yet the dilemmas that he faces – avoiding bullies, missing his dad, falling in love for the first time – seemed so universal. I knew such a complex but sympathetic character would make a fascinating centre for a piece of drama, so I accepted Dani's challenge.

Firstly, I re-read the novel, taking lots of notes. Dani and I then met to share ideas. We agreed that we wanted to create a dark, fast-moving, free-flowing piece of theatre. We cut some scenes and made some alterations to the order of the scenes (a novelist is lucky not to have to worry about costume and set changes!) We also talked through a few key moments, trying to imagine the most effective ways of staging them. I then went away and wrote the script, taking in suggestions from Dani, Tim and our designer, Kate Bunce, and eventually trying scenes out with the actors.

Adapting another writer's work was a fascinating experience. I found it strangely freeing to have the story, scenes and characters given to me; to be concentrating solely on the dialogue and structure of the script. Yet I also felt a responsibility to Tim and to the story itself that I should create something faithful, not necessarily to every specific detail of the novel, but to its unique spirit. To do this I immersed myself in the storylines, people and places of *Starseeker* with the same intensity as I would if it were a play all of my own – an exhausting but very rewarding experience.

Phil Porter

Introduction by Tim Bowler

When Dani Parr first asked me for permission to stage *Starseeker*, I felt a mixture of delight and fear. Delight because I have always felt *Starseeker* would lend itself beautifully to a stage production if sensitively handled; fear because the original novel has so many complexities that I was mindful of the difficulties for the playwright in adapting it. Somehow the adaptor would have to express the balance between the physical reality of Luke's life and the spiritual elements that underpin it. I had no idea how anyone would go about such a task and was privately concerned that the reductive process needed for adaptation to the stage might overemphasise one aspect of the novel at the expense of the other or – worse still – would simply rip the guts out of my book.

I needn't have worried. The moment Dani told me that Phil Porter would be adapting the novel; I knew we were going to be all right. I couldn't have had a better person handling *Starseeker*. Given his expertise and experience, and knowing that Dani would be working closely with him, I decided to stand back and give them space.

When the first draft appeared, it took my breath away. I hadn't expected at this early stage to find a script that was so completely in harmony with the book. The elements which Phil had cut or changed for reasons of space or theatrical effect were not a problem at all. On the contrary, he had been extraordinarily inventive in the way he used the various scenes in the novel; making adjustments where he felt necessary but never losing the spirit of the story. The areas where the draft didn't work required little comment from me, as Dani and Phil had already highlighted them for revision.

The second draft arrived a few weeks later and I read it with a lump in my throat. It's still there.

Tim Bowler

Cast List

Luke
Mrs Little
Skin
Daz
Miranda
Mum
Roger
Mr Harding
Natalie/Barley
Dad
Daniel (of Heaven Scent
    Perfume Supplies)
Squadron Leader Hutchinson
Mrs Roberts
Mr Roberts

Act One

Scene 1

Luke stands alone in a pool of light. A persistent but shifting humming sound envelops him.

LUKE   Sometimes, I hear a sound.
I hear a lot of sounds,
But sometimes …
Like a humming sound.
Like machinery in a basement.   5
Or sometimes like a roar.
Or sometimes just a murmur,
Like the water on the weir.

He presses a finger against the side of his head. The sound and light become euphoric as Luke gets lost in his fantasy …

LUKE   And sometimes,
When I close my eyes,   10
I feel like I'm flying.
Surrounded by trees,
I'm going up past the branches,
Through the leaves,
Like I'm lighter than air.   15
And it's a daytime sky,
But with flashes of gold,
And above me there's a bright speck of light.
And next to me … Dad.
And we fly towards the light   20
Until it's all we can see,
Until the world is nothing
But light.

*   *   *

A grey light picks out Mrs Little, an old and peculiar-looking woman, standing by a high window, looking out. She is holding a box. The box has a black velvet exterior, thick silver beading on its lid and a brocade tassel. From somewhere behind Mrs Little comes the sound of a girl crying. The sound is not piercing or harrowing, just a sad and steady, heartfelt cry.

Cradling the box with great tenderness, Mrs Little lifts its lid and looks inside. She has seen its contents many times before. To look at them brings both pain and relief. The light on Mrs Little becomes hotter and the girl's cry becomes just slightly more urgent. Mrs Little closes her eyes for a moment. She opens her eyes and closes the box gently. The light and the crying fade away.

*   *   *

Luke stands at the bottom of a drainpipe that runs down the side of Mrs Little's house. He takes hold of the drainpipe and looks up, planning his climb. Skin and Daz are with him.

SKIN   So. We want you to be part of the gang. But we need to know we can trust you.   25

DAZ   We need to know you've got the bottle.

SKIN   You're either for us or against us, Luke. That's the way it is. And you don't want to be against us, if you get my meaning.

Luke begins to climb the drainpipe. He is a skilled climber.

SKIN   That's it. Good boy.   30

DAZ   Good boy, Luke.

SKIN   You know what to do. If you see the box,
       you grab it. It's black velvet and silver. She
       was standing in that window with it, so I
       reckon she keeps it there—   35

DAZ   Obsessed with that box, you are, Skin—

SKIN   Shut up, Daz. If not, you come down to the
       front door and you let us in.

DAZ   Yeah, leave it to the professionals.

SKIN   You got that?   40

DAZ   You got that, Lukey Boy?!

       *The sound of the girl crying comes back. It has a
       peculiar, unreal quality to it. Luke stops climbing.*

SKIN   Don't stop, what have you stopped for?
       She'll be back soon. *(Pause)* Oi!

       *The sound of crying remains but Luke resumes his
       climb.*

SKIN   That's more like it. Now get in.

       *Luke clambers through a window and closes it
       behind him. He finds himself at the top of a
       staircase on a small landing area. There are two
       closed doors in front of him and a staircase
       leading down. The sound of the crying girl
       remains. It feels much closer now. He tentatively
       approaches a door. He puts his ear to the door and
       for a brief moment the sound feels closer still. The
       sound stops abruptly. An eerie silence.*

LUKE   *(whispers)* I won't hurt you. I promise.   45
       I promise I won't hurt you.

Luke nervously puts a hand on the doorknob. He twists and pushes but the door is locked. He kneels down and looks through a keyhole. He sees a bedroom – a bed, a radiator, faded wallpaper, empty shelves – dimly lit by the last of the day's light through a skylight. Suddenly, Natalie's face appears at the keyhole, her eyes wet with tears. She stares at Luke. He draws back from the door, frightened. She begins to cry again as he runs down the stairs.

*   *   *

Luke is now climbing a large oak tree. He climbs with great skill and knows every branch, knot and crevice. He reaches a tree-house and climbs in, out of sight. Seconds later, Skin and Daz arrive at the bottom of the tree, out of breath from running. They take a moment to catch their breath and spit. They speak quietly to one another ...

DAZ Reckon he's up there?

SKIN 'Course he is.

They call out to Luke ...

SKIN *(friendly)* Luke? Luke, you up there, mate?

DAZ We know you're up there, we can see you. 50

SKIN Chuck the rope ladder down, will you, mate?

DAZ Yeah, chuck the rope ladder down.

They speak quietly to one another ...

DAZ We could try and climb it.

SKIN Yeah, we tried that before, remember. Nearly broke my neck. Come on, let's go, 55

he's got to face us soon enough. *(Calls out)*
You got to face us soon enough, Lukey Boy!

DAZ   Yeah! You can't stay in your special little tree
forever, Lukey Boy!

SKIN   Shut up, Daz.   60

*Skin and Daz go. Luke peers out of the tree-house
to check they have gone. He sits in the tree-house
looking out across the forest and up at the night
sky. He hears Natalie crying. He holds onto a
branch, gripping it for comfort. The sound
subsides. He climbs down from the tree-house
silently. He stands at the foot of the tree and
speaks to it ...*

LUKE   'Night.

*As Luke walks away, Skin appears in front of him.
Luke stops.*

SKIN   Hello, Luke.

LUKE   All right, Skin?

*Luke thinks about making a run for it but Daz is
behind him.*

SKIN   All you had to do was leave the front door
open. That was you done. Now we've got to   65
wait 'til she goes out again, all cos you got
freaked out by an empty house.

LUKE   It wasn't empty.

DAZ   'Course it was.

SKIN   Well, we're breaking into that place and   70
you're going to help.

DAZ   Whether you like it or not.

SKIN   We're meeting tomorrow morning, eight o'clock, top of the track, we'll make a new plan, you got that? 75

LUKE   All right. *(Pause)* Can I go now?

Pause.

SKIN   Yeah, 'course.

Pause. Luke starts to walk away but Skin grabs him by the throat.

SKIN   Just as soon as I've taught you a lesson in respect.

*   *   *

Miranda plays her flute without accompaniment – 'The Dance of the Blessed Spirits' by Gluck. After a few bars she stops and goes back over a phrase. She goes over the phrase twice more, slowing it down, getting it right.

Scene 2

Mum and Roger are standing outside the front door of Luke's house. They stand close together, holding one another's hands.

MUM   Thanks, Roger.

ROGER   What for?

MUM   For understanding. With Luke. It's difficult.

ROGER   I know.

Pause.

| MUM | He's just hurting at the moment. | 5 |

ROGER You don't have to explain, honestly, I understand. *(Pause)* I'd better go.

MUM All right. Take care.

ROGER And you.

After a pause, they kiss. After the kiss, they hold each other for a couple of seconds. As they are doing this, Luke arrives, unnoticed by Mum and Roger. His face is cut and swollen. He watches them. Mum goes back into the house. Roger turns and sees Luke.

ROGER Luke.   10

Pause. Roger feels caught out. He notices Luke's injuries.

Are you all right?

LUKE Why shouldn't I be?

ROGER Your face.

LUKE What about it?

Pause.

ROGER You're late back, your mum was worried.   15

LUKE Didn't seem it just now.

ROGER Well, she was. *(Pause)* Luke, I'd like to be able to talk to you. About stuff, about me and your mum, about everything. But, at the moment, I can't. Because I'm nervous—   20

LUKE Nervous of what?

ROGER Of you, I—

LUKE   What, and that's my fault, is it?

ROGER   No.

LUKE   Can't help it if you feel nervous, can I?   25
I can't help the way you feel.

ROGER   I know that.

LUKE   Don't blame me.

ROGER   I don't blame you. I don't blame you for
anything. I just wish—   30

LUKE   Yeah, whatever.

Luke pushes past Roger.

ROGER   Luke.

Luke walks into the house.

ROGER   'Night, Luke.

Roger heads home.

*   *   *

*Miranda practises the flute. Starting with the
phrase she stopped on last time, she plays more
of 'The Dance of the Blessed Spirits'.*

*   *   *

*Luke is sitting on his bed. His mum is cleaning his
face. She has cotton wool and a bowl of
disinfected water.*

MUM   What's happening to you? *(Pause)* You hang
around with those horrible boys, come back   35
late every night. If I ask a question you bite
my head off. You've stopped trying at
school—

LUKE	I try in music.
MUM	Not like you used to. Luke, you've got a gift, 40 but if you neglect that gift, it'll disappear.
LUKE	I'm not neglecting anything.
MUM	You are, you've stopped performing, you hardly do any practice.
LUKE	The stuff they give me's boring, it's too easy. 45 And who says I've stopped performing? I've told Mr Harding I'll play in the concert.
MUM	Well, I'm glad about that.
LUKE	Yeah, so what's the problem?!

He pushes her hand away from his face. She has finished cleaning him anyway, so she hands him an ice pack to hold against his bruised eyes.

MUM	Sooner or later— 50
LUKE	Sooner or later what?
MUM	Sooner or later, you're going to have to talk to me.
LUKE	What are we doing now?
MUM	About Dad. 55
LUKE	Yeah, I don't want to. I already told you that. You said I didn't have to, not if I didn't want to.
MUM	That was two years ago. If you keep bottling it up, we'll never get through this. 60

Luke will not look at her.

MUM	What, you think you're the only one that got hurt?

He still will not look at her.

MUM   It's difficult for me too, you know.

Luke shakes his head.

MUM   What? If you've got something to say, why don't
        you say it?   65

LUKE   It didn't look too difficult on the porch just
        now. *(Pause)* He's asked you to marry him,
        hasn't he? *(Pause)* And what did you say?

MUM   I said I'd think about it.

*The sound of Natalie crying comes back, quietly at
first ...*

LUKE   What's there to think about? You're going to   70
        say yes.

MUM   Would you hate it if I did?

LUKE   Well, it's nothing to do with me, is it?

MUM   Of course it is. Luke, you're all I've got.

LUKE   No I'm not, you've got Mr Gillmore.   75

MUM   For goodness' sake, his name's Roger, call him
        Roger! Why don't you like him? Is it because
        you think he's going to take me away from
        you? Or is it just because he isn't Dad?

*The crying is very loud now. Luke is clutching his
head.*

MUM   What's the matter?   80

LUKE   Nothing is—

MUM   Luke?

LUKE   Nothing!

The sound goes. Silence.

LUKE I just can't deal with this whole marriage thing right now, okay? Got too much on my mind. 85

MUM Okay. *(Pause)* I understand that. *(Pause)* I love you.

Mum waits for a response but doesn' t get one. She goes. Luke stands, closes his eyes and takes deep breaths. The euphoric sound and light of Luke's flying fantasy come back.

Scene 3

Luke is lying on the grass by a brook. A bridge passes over the brook just behind Luke. It is morning and the sun is shining. Luke is asleep. Skin and Daz appear on the bridge above him. They stand over him for a moment but he doesn' t wake up ...

SKIN So, what are you doing here, Luke?

Luke wakes up. Skin and Daz join Luke on the ground ...

LUKE All right, Skin.

SKIN I thought we were meeting at The Grange. Thought we had an agreement.

LUKE I was about to go. 5

SKIN Yeah, you were meant to be there half an hour ago.

LUKE I didn't know what time.

SKIN You deaf? I said eight.

DAZ   Eight o'clock.   10

LUKE   I thought you said half past.

SKIN   *(grabbing Luke's throat)* Don't muck me about, Luke. I don't like it when people muck me about, you know that. Why do you muck me about like this?   15

DAZ   He reckons he's too good for us, that's why.

SKIN   Is that it? Do you reckon you're too good for us?

DAZ   Cos he plays the piano.

SKIN   Is that what it is?

LUKE   No—   20

SKIN   Does mummy not want you hanging round with us?

LUKE   None of her business who I hang round with.

SKIN   *(lets go of Luke's throat with a push)* Right. So we'll see you at midnight. Just up from The   25 Grange. You can make up for last time.

LUKE   What, break in again?

DAZ   He's quick, ain't he? You're quick.

LUKE   Tonight?

SKIN   I just said so, didn't I?   30

LUKE   But she'll be in the house. I thought that was the point, do it on a Friday evening when she's at the shop. She'll hear me.

SKIN   At midnight? She'll be asleep.

LUKE   Yeah, what if she wakes up though?   35

SKIN   Then you run away, don't you?

DAZ   Yeah, you're good at running away, ain't you, Lukey?

LUKE	Come on, Skin, I'd get done by the police. Why's it got to be me?	40

SKIN What's the matter with you? You should be pleased we want you in the gang. And you know why it's got to be you. Cos you're the best at climbing, ain't you, Monkey Boy? And cos you know your way round the house 45 now, don't you, after your last little visit? And because you owe me for messing it up last time, all right? You owe me big time, Luke Stanton.

Miranda appears.

MIRANDA Luke? 50

SKIN Oh, hello, Miranda.

DAZ Hello, Miranda.

MIRANDA Hi. Luke—

SKIN How are you?

MIRANDA Fine, thank you— 55

SKIN Still riding?

Daz sniggers.

MIRANDA Pardon?

SKIN Still riding that horse? Only I haven't seen you go past my house lately. Used to really like that, I did, watching you come past. 60
(He leers at Miranda) So, what can we do for you, beautiful?

MIRANDA Nothing. I want to speak to Luke.

SKIN Oh, I'm sorry, you should have said. How very rude of us. Come on, Daz, let's leave them 65 to it, shall we? Don't want to stand in the way of true love. We're all sorted here anyway, ain't we, Lukey?

LUKE Yeah.

SKIN Good. I'm pleased. Later then. 70

DAZ Yeah, later, Lukey.

Skin and Daz go. Pause.

MIRANDA What happened to your face?

LUKE Nothing.

MIRANDA Were you in a fight or something?

LUKE It doesn't matter. 75

MIRANDA Did they do it? *(Pause)* Why do you hang round with them, Luke? It doesn't make any sense. They're horrible. And they stink—

LUKE Just leave it, I said it's not a problem. *(Pause)* What did you want? 80

MIRANDA Oh. It's nothing really—

LUKE Okay, well, I'd better go, so—

MIRANDA No, hang on, don't go. I mean, it's not nothing, there is something. Can you help me with something? 85

LUKE What?

MIRANDA Well, I told Mr Harding I'd do a flute piece at the concert. But the thing is, I need someone to do the piano part.

LUKE Yeah, sorry, I'm already doing a piece. 90

MIRANDA I know that, but ... I mean, you're so good and everything, I thought maybe you could do both.

LUKE	Can't Melanie do it?
MIRANDA	Yeah, if you don't want to. It's just she's a bit, you know … *(She does an impression of Melanie's piano playing)* I just thought … Because I'm not much good, so I thought if you played, because you're so good, I thought it might cover up my mistakes. But if you don't want to—
LUKE	Okay.
MIRANDA	What, you'll do it?
LUKE	Why not?
MIRANDA	Really?
LUKE	'Course.
MIRANDA	That's brilliant. It's called 'The Dance of the Blessed Spirits'.
LUKE	No problem.
MIRANDA	Thanks. Honestly, I've been getting in such a state. So, if I give you a ring later, could we sort out a practice session?
LUKE	If you like.
MIRANDA	That would be great, thanks so much. *(Pause)* See, it's not that hard, is it?
LUKE	What?
MIRANDA	To be the real you. Instead of all this other stuff.

95

100

105

110

115

Luke smiles. Miranda goes. The soundscape begins to alter. At first, it is just a subtle change in the 'real' sounds that surround Luke. The birdsong and the sound of the brook take on a peculiar,

*invasive quality. But soon they give way to a
sound that is familiar from the beginning of Act
One, Scene 1 – a persistent, vibrating hum. After
a time, that sound builds and deepens to become
a roar, both menacing and appealing ...*

LUKE   That sound again.
That humming sound.   120
Only stronger now.
Like a rumble this time.
Like thunder this time.
Like a wave getting closer.
Like a tidal wave   125
But all around.

*The sound of a piano emerges from within the
roar: Tchaikovsky's 'Douce Rêverie'.*

LUKE   Then piano music.
Childish …
Child music.
It's beautiful.   130
I know this music.
What is it?

*All sound but the piano music fades away. The
music leads us into Scene 4.*

Scene 4

*Luke is standing in the middle of Mr Harding's
teaching room. Mr Harding is sitting in a chair.
There is a piano. Luke is lost in 'Douce Rêverie'.*

HARDING   Come and sit down.

Luke does not hear Mr Harding, only the music.

HARDING Luke?

LUKE *(to himself)* What is it?

The music fades away. Luke turns to look at Mr Harding.

HARDING Come and sit down.

LUKE Don't you want me to play?   5

HARDING Not just now.

Luke sits with Mr Harding. Mr Harding stares at Luke. The sound of a bouncing ball invades Luke's head.

HARDING We'll make this lesson a freebie. Since we're just sitting around.

The ball bounces some more and a child laughs.

HARDING What are you hearing, Luke?

A mysterious cacophony erupts: the bouncing ball, the laughing child, the mad scuttling of insects, that familiar humming sound. He presses a finger against the side of his head. The other sounds die out, leaving only the humming sound. A few notes from 'Douce Rêverie' are heard over the hum before Luke's head becomes quiet again.

HARDING The isle is full of noises.   10

LUKE What's that supposed to mean?

HARDING It's a quotation. *(Pause)* Do you know what I see when I look at you? I see a person made of music. I see a person consumed by music. I

see a person with the capacity to experience 15
music and sound and life in a way that's
beyond even the imagination of ordinary
people like me. What an amazing thing,
Luke! What a gift! *(Pause)* What I'm saying is,
if life's getting difficult, let your gift guide 20
you. Let it help you—

LUKE   I don't need any help.

HARDING   Well I think you do. I think you're at war.

LUKE   Who with?

HARDING   Everyone. Especially yourself. 25

LUKE   I don't need this.

HARDING   Look at you.

LUKE   I don't need this!

HARDING   Okay.

LUKE   Why can't people leave me alone?! 30

HARDING   All right, Luke, I'm sorry. I'm worried about you,
that's all. A lot of people are.

Pause. Six notes from 'Douce Rêverie'.

LUKE   Mr Harding?

HARDING   Yes?

LUKE   Have you got the sheet music for 'Scenes 35
From Childhood'?

HARDING   No, I lent it to someone. Why?

LUKE   Or 'The Children's Corner Suite'?

HARDING   I thought you didn't like Debussy. *(Pause)* Is this
for the concert? 40

LUKE   No, something else.

*Intrigued, Mr Harding begins a search for 'The
Children's Corner Suite'.*

LUKE   Anyway, I thought you wanted me to play that
        other piece for the concert.

HARDING I've been thinking about that. Why don't you
        play something different? It's your last   45
        concert and it's my last concert, play
        something you really want to play. *(He finds
        'The Children's Corner Suite')* 'The Children's
        Corner Suite' by Claude Debussy.

        *Luke takes the music from Mr Harding and rifles
        through it in search of the childlike tune in his
        head.*

HARDING In fact, don't even tell me what you're going   50
        to play. Surprise me. Play something that
        means something to you. *(He sees that Luke is
        hardly listening)* Got what you wanted?

LUKE   Not really.

HARDING 'The Snow Is Dancing', that's a nice piece.   55
        Play it for me.

        Luke sits at the piano and plays.

HARDING The isle is full of noises.

        Luke continues to play, leading us into Scene 5.

Scene 5

*A laptop computer glows invitingly on a desk in a
dark room. Luke sits at the desk to check his email
account. He clicks the mouse twice and then types.
He speaks the words that he types ...*

25

LUKE Username lukestanton92. Password peanut. *(Click)* Inbox. Jason Skinner. *(Click. Skin appears)*

SKIN Midnight. Or else.

Pause.

LUKE *(Click. Skin disappears)* Inbox. Miranda Davis. *(Click. Miranda appears)*

MIRANDA Hi Luke. Thanks so much for saying you'll 5 help me with my piece. Now the piano bit will be good, even if the flute bits are rubbish. I tried it with Melanie, which was okay, but she fidgets and sniffs a lot, which puts me off. Are you free tomorrow at eleven 10 to practice? You could come to mine and use our piano or I could come to you. Thanks again, this means such a lot to me. Love, Miranda. Smiley face, kiss kiss. Kiss.

LUKE Reply. *(Click. He types …)* Tomorrow at eleven 15 is fine. See you at yours. Luke. Send. *(Click. Miranda disappears)*

Luke sits back in his chair. His head fills with the humming sound, which morphs into the sound of an aeroplane overhead. Silence.

LUKE Log out. *(Click)* Log in. *(Click)* Username kirstistanton. Password edvardgrieg. *(Click)* Inbox. Roger Gillmore. *(Pause. Click. Roger appears)*

ROGER Kirsti, I'll wait forever if that's what it takes. 20 All my love, Roger.

Pause. Luke thumps the desk. Pause. Luke thumps the desk three more times. He fights back tears.

LUKE   Logout. *(Click)* Login. *(Click)* lukestanton92. *(Click)* New message. *(Click)* To dad@heaven.com. Why? Why won't you speak to me? *(Pause)* Send. *(Click)*   25

Pause. Luke closes the computer. Pause, Luke sits with his head in his hands.

Quite suddenly, somewhere else in the house, someone begins to play the piano. Amazed, Luke listens. After a few seconds, the music stops in the middle of a bar. Pause. The pianist returns to the beginning of the piece. We can see the pianist now – a graceful, silhouetted, ghostly figure playing with great poise and control. The music stops in the same place. Pause. Luke walks towards the piano as the pianist plays the piece again. He recognises the pianist as his dad. As the music stops, again in the same place, the stage is plunged into darkness. Luke switches on a light. The pianist is gone. Luke sits at the piano and plays the same piece. The pianist appears behind Luke, watching over his shoulder. Luke finds he cannot take the music any further than the ghostly pianist, and stops in just the same place. Pause. Luke slams the piano shut.

Scene 6

Luke stands at the bottom of the drainpipe that runs down the side of Mrs Little's house, as in Act One, Scene 1. Skin and Daz are with him.

SKIN   Now remember, it's different this time. She's in, so you got to be quiet.

DAZ   Yeah, quiet as a ickle baby mouse. Squeak!

SKIN   Shut up, Daz.

DAZ   Squeak!   5

SKIN   Shut up, Daz! *(Pause)* When you get in, just look for the box, don't muck about with nothing else. All we want right now is the box.

LUKE   What if it's in her bedroom?

SKIN   Then you'll have to be extra quiet, won't   10 you? So as not to wake her up. Go on then, up you go.

Pause. Luke begins his climb.

SKIN   That's it. Don't you let us down now, Luke. Cos we're going to be right here waiting for you.

DAZ   Yeah, don't let us down, Luke.   15

Pause. Luke climbs through the window and finds himself back on the landing with two closed doors and a flight of stairs leading down. He tentatively approaches the door to Natalie's room. He puts a hand against the door.

LUKE   Hello?

He twists the doorknob and finds that the room is not locked. He enters the room. The bed is covered with a swirl of bed sheets. Luke believes Natalie may be hiding beneath them.

LUKE   Don't scream. Please don't scream. I won't hurt you, I promise. I'm your friend.

*He reaches out and touches the bed sheets. She is
not there. Pause. He leaves the room. He
approaches the other closed door. The door
squeals on its hinges as he opens it. It is another
bedroom. A similar swirl of bed sheets on the bed.
Luke sees the box on the other side of the room.
He moves silently across to it and picks it up. As
he does so, Mrs Little appears behind him. She
has a stick in one hand and a cordless phone in
the other.*

LITTLE   Put that down.

*Luke turns to see Mrs Little. She is pointing her
stick at him.*

LITTLE   Don't even think about running, Luke   20
          Stanton. You'll only make things worse for
          yourself. I've phoned the police, they'll be
          here very soon. *(Pause)* So, it was you that
          broke in last night too, was it? She told me
          you frightened her. *(Pause)* It's all right, you   25
          can come out now, he won't hurt you.

          *Natalie appears from the swirl of bed sheets.
          Natalie is blind.*

LITTLE   I'm here, darling. Nana's here.

          Natalie clings to Mrs Little.

LITTLE   It's him. The boy from last night. Don't you
          want to say hello?

          Natalie clings tighter.

LITTLE   She's been upset all day after your little visit.   30
          That's why she's in here with me tonight.

LUKE I'm not going to hurt her.

LITTLE I know that. I know you're not like the thugs you're stupid enough to hang around with. *(Pause)* I didn't really call the police. 35

LUKE What?

LITTLE Say pardon, not what.

LUKE Sorry.

LITTLE I said I didn't really call the police. But that's not to say I won't. *(To Natalie)* Get into bed 40 now. Good girl.

Natalie gets into bed. Mrs Little tucks her in.

LITTLE Nana be back very soon. Good girl.

Mrs Little walks out of the bedroom.

LITTLE *(to Luke)* Follow me.

Luke follows her down the stairs to the kitchen.

LITTLE Sit down.

Luke does not sit.

LITTLE Or run if you like. I'll have phoned the 45 police before you reach the end of the road.

Luke sits at the kitchen table.

LITTLE I've been hearing a lot about you and your gang.

LUKE Who from?

LITTLE Miss Grubb and her customers. They talk 50 about Jason Skinner and how he's destined for prison. And Darren Fisher and how he bullies money out of the younger children. But mostly they talk about you.

LUKE   What do they say?   55

LITTLE They say you're special.

LUKE   Why do they say that?

LITTLE They say you're gifted. You're Matthew Stanton's son, aren't you? And you play the piano. Like he did.   60

LUKE   Yeah. Like he did.

LITTLE I read about the cancer. *(Pause)* Your father was a wonderful musician. I saw him play ten years ago—

LUKE   I don't want to talk about this—   65

LITTLE He was incredible—

LUKE   I just told you, I don't want to talk about this. You deaf or something? I don't want to talk about it. *(Pause)* I'm going home. Do what you like about the police.   70

LITTLE And what about the girl?

LUKE   What about her?

LITTLE You can help her.

LUKE   How? She's frightened of me.

LITTLE She's terrified of you.   75

LUKE   So I can't help, can I?

LITTLE Stay there.

Mrs Little hurriedly fetches a tin. She opens the tin and takes out some money. She holds it out to Luke.

LITTLE	Take this.
LUKE	What for?
LITTLE	Something to show your friends. I know 80 they're waiting outside for you. When you come back, I'll tell you how you can help.
LUKE	I don't want your money.
LITTLE	Take it.
LUKE	No, and I'm not coming back. 85
LITTLE	But you have to.
LUKE	Sorry—
LITTLE	She needs you.
LUKE	I can't get involved in this.
LITTLE	She needs your help. 90

Luke does not take the money. Natalie comes into the kitchen.

LITTLE	Please.
NATALIE	Nana …?
LITTLE	Come here, darling.

Natalie moves across to Mrs Little. Mrs Little wipes Natalie's face dry with a handkerchief.

LITTLE	*(to Luke. Cold)* Please come back.

*   *   *

Skin and Daz close in on Luke.

SKIN	So? What happened? 95
LUKE	I didn't get the box.
SKIN	We can see that.

LUKE   Well, there was nothing else worth nicking.

DAZ   Yeah, right.

LUKE   Honest. Just a load of ornaments and tacky   100
stuff.

SKIN   Where did you look?

LUKE   Everywhere.

DAZ   What, every room?

LUKE   Yeah.   105

SKIN   And what about the old woman?

LUKE   Didn't see her.

SKIN   But you went in every room?

LUKE   Yeah—

DAZ   So you must have seen her.   110

LUKE   Yeah, but what I mean is …

SKIN   What do you mean, Luke?

LUKE   I saw her but she didn't see me, she was asleep.

SKIN   Which room?

LUKE   The one at the top, far side.   115

DAZ   Was she wearing curlers?

LUKE   No.

DAZ   Bet she looked well ugly—

SKIN   Shut up, Daz. *(Pause. To Luke)* Carry on.

LUKE   Nothing more to tell.   120

SKIN   You sure about that?

Pause. Skin grabs Luke's hands.

LUKE   Come on, Skin—

| SKIN | I just want to look at them. *(He studies Luke's hands)* Good hands these, Luke. Very good hands. No wonder you're so good at climbing. And playing the piano. | 125 |

LUKE Glad you like them. Can I have them back now?

SKIN Do you click the joints? Daz clicks the joints, makes them pop, don't you, Daz?

DAZ Sometimes, yeah. *(Pops a knuckle)* 130

SKIN That's it. Can you do that, Luke?

LUKE No.

SKIN Doesn't hurt. I'll do it for you.

Skin starts pulling on Luke's fingers.

LUKE Don't.

SKIN Keep still. Got to be careful. Else they might break. 135

LUKE Please—

SKIN You're lying to me, Luke.

LUKE I'm not lying.

SKIN The old bird was asleep, was she? 140

LUKE Yeah.

SKIN And she didn't wake up?

LUKE No.

SKIN So how come the kitchen light went on?

DAZ Did it? 145

SKIN Yes it did, why did the kitchen light come on, Luke?

LUKE Cos I needed to see better.

| SKIN | So why didn't you turn the lights on in the other rooms? | 150 |

| LUKE | Kitchen's the furthest from her bedroom. I didn't want to wake her up. Can you let go of my hands? |

| SKIN | Why were you in the kitchen so long? |

| LUKE | Can you let go of my hands? | 155 |

| SKIN | When I'm ready. Why were you in the kitchen so long? |

| LUKE | I was looking through the drawers. For the box. |

Pause. Skin lets go of Luke's hands. Pause. He grabs him by the throat.

| SKIN | Just remember, you're still in one piece cos that's how I need you right now. And if you want to stay that way, you'll do exactly what I say. Got that? | 160 |

| LUKE | Yeah … |

| SKIN | Don't you lie to me, Luke, don't you ever lie to me. | 165 |

| LUKE | I'm not. |

Pause. Skin lets go of Luke.

| SKIN | Tomorrow afternoon. Usual time, usual place. |

Skin goes. Daz follows after Skin.

Scene 7

The humming sound returns. Luke approaches a gravestone and kneels in front of it. The childish tune ('Douce Rêverie') and the unfinished tune

*from Act One, Scene 5 play in his head, fading in
and out, competing for attention. He hears
Natalie's desperate voice: 'Nana, Nana ...'. The
sounds fade away.*

*   *   *

*Luke turns to see Miranda. She is sitting near a
piano with her back to him. She is holding her
flute.*

LUKE   Miranda?

She turns to look at him. She is upset.

LUKE   I'm sorry.

MIRANDA   What for?

LUKE   Being late.

MIRANDA   Don't apologise. I'm sure you're very busy.   5

LUKE   It's not that—

MIRANDA   Honestly, it's no big deal. I mean it's a pretty
            stupid idea anyway, don't you think? You
            accompanying me. With me being useless
            and you being brilliant. So, you know,   10
            maybe we shouldn't bother—

LUKE   Listen—

MIRANDA   Because I can understand if it's boring for you.
            But just don't tell me you're going to help me
            if you don't want to. Because, you know, it   15
            might sound silly to you, but this is actually
            quite important to me—

LUKE   Yeah, but I do want to.

MIRANDA   You don't, you're two hours late—

LUKE   But listen, I do. I just … I'm not doing much   20
         right at the moment, you know? Something's
         happening to me, I'm feeling really kind of
         messed up, I can't explain it.

         Pause. Miranda's attitude softens.

MIRANDA Do you want to try?

LUKE   I don't know. My mum's got Roger coming   25
         round the whole time, and that's doing my
         head in. And other stuff too that I can't really
         talk about.

MIRANDA It's okay.

LUKE   It's not though, is it? I mean, I didn't mean   30
         to make you think like I don't care. *(Pause)* I
         was at my dad's grave, that's why I was late.
         Not cos I don't want to accompany you.

         Pause.

MIRANDA Luke, I'm not going to tell you I understand.
         Because I don't. But I want to help. So, if   35
         you want to talk or anything …

         Luke smiles. Pause.

LUKE   Shall we try the music?

MIRANDA *(a joke)* Well, only if you've got time. I mean,
         since your life's completely falling to
         pieces—   40

LUKE   *(he gets the joke)* I didn't say that—

MIRANDA Since your life's nothing but a dark pit of
         despair—

LUKE   Shut up.

MIRANDA   I mean, maybe you should be sorting that   45
out. I don't want you making mistakes and
spoiling my beautiful flute-playing, do I?

Luke sits at the piano.

LUKE   Yeah, right. It'd take more than that to muck
up my piano playing. What page is it?

MIRANDA   Twenty-nine.   50

Luke finds the music in the book on the piano.

MIRANDA   Okay, you're going to have to be really patient
with me.

LUKE   That's okay.

MIRANDA   I'll probably stop a lot. And make loads of
mistakes and stuff.   55

LUKE   That's what practice is for.

MIRANDA   I feel kind of nervous with you. I can get
through the whole thing, just as long as I
don't go too fast.

LUKE   That's all right, it's not meant to be fast.   60
How's this?

*Luke begins to play 'The Dance of the Blessed
Spirits'. Miranda nods.*

LUKE   *(over the music)* Okay, stop and start as much as
you like. I'll play around you.

*Luke and Miranda play. Miranda plays nervously
to begin with, but she soon relaxes and plays the
piece well.*

*   *   *

As the music continues, Mrs Little signs a letter,
puts it in an envelope, seals it and addresses it.
The special box is on the table in front of her.

Scene 8

Again, the laptop computer glows invitingly in the
darkness. Luke moves across and sits at it. He
clicks the mouse twice and then types. As before,
he speaks the words that he types …

LUKE   Username lukestanton92. Password peanut.
        (Click) Inbox. Heaven.

        Luke is astonished. For a moment, he is unsure
        whether he wants to read the email but he decides
        he must. Click. Daniel, a man in a suit, appears.

DANIEL Hello there! We have searched our records
        and have no record of you contacting us
        prior to yesterday's email. Would you be so   5
        kind as to make your enquiry stroke order
        again? Thank you and our apologies for any
        inconvenience, Heaven Scent Natural
        Perfume Supplies.

        Luke is despondent. Click. Daniel disappears.

LUKE   Inbox. Kirsti Stanton.   10

        Click. Mum appears.

MUM   I love you, Luke. *(Pause)* Luke?

        Luke turns in surprise. Mum is really in the room
        now.

LUKE   Mum.

MUM   Are you hungry? I'll make you a sandwich if you like.

LUKE   No, thanks.   15

She joins him at the table.

LUKE   Thanks for the email.

MUM   I meant it.

Pause.

MUM   I've never stopped loving your dad. You know that, don't you?

LUKE   Don't.   20

MUM   What?

LUKE   I can't deal with it. When you talk like this.

MUM   But I want you to understand. I couldn't stop loving him any more than I could stop loving you. But love's a strange thing. You think   25 you've lost it then it creeps up on you again. When your dad died, I really didn't think I'd love again. I don't know, I still don't know how I feel about Roger.

LUKE   You like him.   30

MUM   Of course I like him.

LUKE   I can tell from how you are with him.

MUM   What do you mean?

LUKE   You're different with him. Excited and stuff. And he's the same. I can hear it in your   35 voices.

MUM   You hear lots of things, don't you? Like your dad. *(Pause)* I just feel confused more than

anything. And guilty that I'm hurting you.
But I know your dad would want me to   40
find new love. If that's what made me happy.

LUKE   And does it?

MUM   Not really. Not when I know that it makes you
unhappy. Can you imagine a future where it
didn't make you unhappy?   45

Luke cannot look at her.

MUM   Sure you're not hungry?

Luke does not respond.

MUM   It'll be okay. I promise. *(Pause)* And anyway, I'm
not the only one with an admirer.

Luke looks up.

MUM   Don't hurt her feelings, Luke.

LUKE   I won't.   50

MUM   Miranda's a nice girl.

LUKE   I know.

MUM   She's sensitive. So don't—

LUKE   I won't. She doesn't feel that way about me
anyway.   55

MUM   Oh, right, of course she doesn't. *(She gives him
an envelope)* So who else is hand-posting you
letters? Lovely handwriting she's got. Kind of
old-fashioned.

*Mum goes. Luke stares at the letter. As he opens
it, the computer makes a noise, indicating a new
email. He puts the letter down and opens the
laptop.*

LUKE	Inbox. Jason Skinner. *(Click. Skin appears)*	60
SKIN	Midnight. Be there.	
LUKE	*(to the screen)* I don't think so, Skin. *(Click)*	

Skin disappears. Luke closes the laptop, resolute but frightened. He hears the humming sound, very distant, as if its source is somewhere else in the house. He follows the sound. It leads him to his bedroom.

*   *   *

As Luke enters his room, the sound becomes more intense. He hears Miranda playing the flute, a harp, rushing water, ravenous insects, Mr Harding mumbling in his sleep. The sounds come together to form an ethereal symphony. He sits on his bed and closes his eyes. The sounds now merge to form the tidal roar and Luke is flooded by a brilliant blue.

LUKE The flashes of gold form a circle.
Form a circle round the speck of light.
And we're flying closer now.   65
And I can see it now.
And it's not just a speck, it's a star.
A five-pointed star.
We're flying towards it.
We're being dragged in.   70
But not just our bodies,
Everything …

The roar becomes euphoric. Skin and Daz appear on the street below Luke's room. Skin makes a 'fssssst' sound to attract Luke's attention. He makes the sound several times. The roar implodes and Luke's head becomes silent.

SKIN Fsssssst. Luke. Fsssssst.

Luke opens his window.

LUKE All right, Skin.

SKIN *(hisses)* What do you think you're playing at? 75
It's one. I said midnight. *(Pause)* Come on
then, are you coming or what? *(Pause)* I said
are you coming or what?!

LUKE I can't.

SKIN What did you say? 80

LUKE I said I can't come out. I'm not coming.

Skin is stunned.

SKIN You're dead, Luke. You are so dead!

Scene 9

Mrs Little's house. Mrs Little regards Luke with suspicion.

LITTLE Does anyone know you're here?

LUKE No.

LITTLE What about your friends?

LUKE What friends?

LITTLE Darren and Jason. 5

LUKE They're not my friends.

LITTLE And what about your mother?

LUKE She thinks I'm at school.

LITTLE   And what will the school do when you don't
         turn up?   10

LUKE   Nothing. They think I'm ill. I emailed the
         secretary.

LITTLE   And that's acceptable, is it?

LUKE   I sent it from my mum's email account.

LITTLE   No-one can know that you're here.   15

LUKE   You said in your letter.

LITTLE   *(to herself)* Good.

LUKE   What?

LITTLE   Don't say what, say pardon. If we're going to
         spend time together, you'll show me some   20
         manners.

LUKE   Who says we're going to spend time together?

LITTLE   Well, you're here now, aren't you?

LUKE   Doesn't mean I'll come again.

LITTLE   That's your choice, but if you don't I'll tell   25
         the police about the break-ins. *(Pause)* I want
         you to help my granddaughter.

LUKE   How am I supposed to help?

LITTLE   I'll tell you. But first, promise that your visits
         will remain a secret. You say nothing, I'll say 30
         nothing.

LUKE   Fine.

         She stares at him.

LUKE   All right, I promise.

         Pause.

LITTLE   Sit down.

Luke sits.

LITTLE   Natalie has a learning disability. Two years   35
ago, she was in a car crash in which her
mother and father were both killed. Since
the crash she's become very confused and
frightened. She's unsure of everything, who
she is, who her parents were, who I am—   40

LUKE   She calls you Nana.

LITTLE   I taught her that but she doesn't understand
what it means.

Pause.

LUKE   Has she always been blind?

LITTLE   No, that happened in the crash. She was   45
blinded by glass from the windscreen.

Pause. Luke stands as if to leave.

LUKE   This isn't my problem—

LITTLE   I'm not finished yet, let me finish!

Reluctantly, Luke sits.

LITTLE   Ever since the crash, she's been living here.

LUKE   She's been living here two whole years?   50

LITTLE   Yes, but she's not been out of the house in that
time.

LUKE   In two years? Why not?

LITTLE   It would frighten her. And besides, I'm not
supposed to have her.   55

Pause.

LUKE   What do you mean?

Pause.

LITTLE   When the accident happened I was living in
India. I'd been a nurse there. I couldn't get a
flight to England until after the funeral, by
which time Natalie was in a home. She was   60
receiving a level of care that I didn't consider
adequate, so I took her away.

LUKE   What, you stole her?

LITTLE   It was in her best interests.

LUKE   But you're related. They would have let you   65
take her anyway.

LITTLE   They would have said an old woman like me
couldn't cope with Natalie's special needs.
Well, that's a joke if you've seen the home
she was in. She needs constant attention.   70

LUKE   Is that why you don't go out? I thought you just
didn't like people very much.

LITTLE   I don't.

Pause.

LUKE   I still don't see how I can help.

LITTLE   I want you to play for her. You're very good,   75
I'm told.

LUKE   How's me playing the piano going to help?

Pause.

LITTLE   I hired a piano-tuner. Once he'd finished
tuning, he played. She could hear it from her

room. It made her happy. I'd never seen her   80
so peaceful.

LUKE   Can't you just put the radio on?

LITTLE   It doesn't have the same effect.

LUKE   Why have you got a piano if you can't play?

LITTLE   That's none of your business.   85

LUKE   And why keep it tuned if no-one uses it?

LITTLE   You're not here to ask questions, you're here
to play.

LUKE   Is that an order?

Pause.

LITTLE   No. It's a request. I would like it if you   90
would play. For my granddaughter.

Luke sits at the piano.

LUKE   What do you want me to play?

LITTLE   Anything. Anything you like.

*Luke plays the piano. Mrs Little leaves the room.
He plays alone. After a few moments, Natalie
comes into the room, fragile and dishevelled. Luke
senses her presence. He stops playing and turns.
They face one another.*

Act Two

Scene 1

Mrs Little's house, a few minutes later. Luke is playing 'Pavane' by Ravel. Mrs Little and Natalie stand together. They listen absorbedly. The music comes to an end. Pause.

LITTLE   I'll make some tea. You'll stay and play some more, won't you? You'd like to hear some more, wouldn't you, Natalie?

Natalie wants more music. Mrs Little goes to make tea.

LUKE   Hello, Natalie.

Natalie backs away from the piano.

LUKE   It's all right. I'll play some more, shall I? I'll   5
play some more.

Luke plays 'Nocturne' by Grieg. As the music progresses, Natalie edges towards Luke. He senses her moving in and plays especially softly so as not to distress her. Natalie plays a note on the piano. She plays the note a few times, getting louder. Luke stops playing.

LUKE   Do you want to play?

Natalie reaches out and touches Luke's face.

NATALIE   Ears …

LUKE   That's right. They're my ears.

NATALIE   Funny …   10

LUKE	You find them funny?
NATALIE	Funny ears.
LUKE	Maybe I find your ears funny.

He touches her ear but she recoils.

| LUKE | Don't worry. I won't hurt you. |

He puts a hand on her shoulder. She moves closer and snuggles against him. They stay like this for a little while. He looks up and sees a clock on the wall.

LUKE	Four o'clock … Miranda! *(He gets up to leave)* 15 Natalie, I'll come back soon, okay? I'll come back and play again soon. *(Calls out)* Mrs Little, I've got to go.
LITTLE	*(off)* I beg your pardon.
LUKE	I'm late, I've got to go. 20
LITTLE	*(off)* But I've made tea.
LUKE	Yeah, sorry. I'll come back soon, I promise.

Luke leaves Natalie at the piano. She runs her hands across the keys.

*   *   *

Outside Luke's house. Luke is hurriedly walking past on his way to meet Miranda. A light is switched on in an upstairs room. He looks up to see his Dad, standing at the window, looking down at him.

| LUKE | Dad? |

Dad disappears to be replaced by Roger. Roger does not see Luke. He is joined by Mum. He kisses her tenderly. Mum draws a curtain, shutting Luke out.

*   *   *

The graveyard. Luke sits by his dad's headstone, deep in tortured thought. Miranda appears.

MIRANDA   I thought I'd find you here. Are you all right? *(Luke doesn't reply)* Luke? You weren't in   25
school. Are you ill or something?

LUKE   No.

MIRANDA   Only … you said you'd come over for a rehearsal. I thought maybe—

LUKE   What, that I'd stood you up again?   30

MIRANDA   No, just that something might be wrong. So I came to look for you. I went to your tree. I would have phoned but I didn't want to get you in trouble. If, like, your mum didn't know you weren't in school or something.   35

Luke buries his face in his hands and cries. For a moment, Miranda is not sure what to do. She sits next to Luke and puts an arm around him. He stops crying.

MIRANDA   What is it? Is it Jason Skinner? He was asking where you were today. Has he … done something to you?

LUKE   Not yet.

MIRANDA   What does that mean?   40

LUKE   It doesn't matter. It's not them anyway.

MIRANDA   Then what is it?

LUKE   It's not the same any more.

MIRANDA   What isn't?

LUKE   With mum.   45

MIRANDA   In what way?

LUKE   I saw them just now. Kissing. I was walking past
the house on the way to yours. They were in
the window.

MIRANDA   Did they see you?   50

LUKE   No. It's just … I can't deal with that. It's not
right. And the way it looked. I can't deal with
it.

Pause.

MIRANDA   Luke, I know you don't want to hear this right
now, but Roger's a nice man.   55

LUKE   My dad was a nice man.

MIRANDA   I know. *(Pause)* Okay, if your dad was here now,
if you could ask him about your mum and
Roger, what do you think he'd say?

LUKE   Well, he's not here, is he?   60

MIRANDA   Yeah, but just imagine—

LUKE   But he's not! He's gone! That's what happens
when you die, you disappear! *(Pause)* I'm
sorry.

MIRANDA   It's okay.   65

LUKE   I shouldn't have shouted.

MIRANDA   I'm fine.

LUKE   What's the matter with me?! *(Pause)* Do you
       want to go and rehearse?

MIRANDA   Only if you want to. I mean, if you'd rather   70
          just go home …

LUKE   Go home? What would I want to go there for?
       (He stands and helps her up) Come on. We'll
       get an hour in before tea if we go now.

Scene 2

*Luke's bedroom. He is exhausted. He enjoys a rare
moment of peace. He hears the opening phrase of
'Rêverie'. He hums it back to himself.*

LUKE   I know that tune …

       *He hums the tune again, getting a few notes
       further into the tune. A light comes up on the
       piano. Dad is at the piano. He plays the first note.*

LUKE   I'm at the old house.

       Dad plays the note again.

LUKE   I must be four years old …

       *Luke hums 'Rêverie' and Dad plays with him. The
       light on the piano gets warmer, sunnier as Dad
       continues to play and Luke speaks …*

LUKE   It's summer.
       All the windows open.   5
       Dad doesn't know I'm there.
       I'm standing in the hallway.
       I don't want it to stop.
       Ever.
       And that's the tune he's playing.   10

And when it finishes, I run into the room.
And he picks me up,
Says, 'Did you like that, Luke?'
And I say, 'Yes.'
And he says, 'Then it's for you.'   15

Skin and Daz appear in the street below.

SKIN   Oi!

*Abruptly, the music stops, the piano slams shut
and Dad is plunged into darkness. Pause.*

SKIN   Oi!

DAZ   Quiet, Skin, his mum'll hear.

SKIN   I don't care who hears!

Luke does not go to the window.

SKIN   I know you're in there, Luke! Well, you listen 20
        to me. You can't hide away forever. Your
        time's going to come. And when I catch you,
        I swear, you'll wish you never crossed me.
        Worst mistake of your life, Luke Stanton.
        Worst mistake of your life!   25

                *   *   *

Natalie is crying.

Scene 3

*The kitchen. Mum is sitting at the table, working
on her laptop. The phone rings. She answers it.*

MUM   Hello?

Pause.

MUM   Hello?

She replaces the receiver. This is not the first time this has happened. She is anxious. Luke comes in.

LUKE   Morning.

MUM   Do you know anything about that?

LUKE   About what?   5

MUM   Happened twice yesterday too. The phone rings, I pick it up and say hello, the line goes dead.

LUKE   Probably some bored nutcase.

MUM   Either that or Jason Skinner. What's going on? 10

LUKE   Nothing.

MUM   Don't lie to me.

LUKE   I'm not. It's not Skin, it's nothing to do with me.

MUM   You're out all the time, you never tell me where you're going, I sometimes even wonder if   15
you're coming back.

LUKE   Well, what time did you get back last night? It was after I went to bed.

Pause. She is upset.

LUKE   Mum …

MUM   It's over, okay?   20

LUKE   What is?

MUM   With Roger.

LUKE   When?

MUM   Last night. That's why I was late back.

Pause.

| LUKE | How? What happened? | 25 |

LUKE How? What happened?   25

MUM Nothing happened.

LUKE Did he do something to hurt you?

MUM Of course he didn't.

LUKE Then … why?

MUM I just decided. For everyone. So you can   30
stop hating him now.

*She turns from him and busies herself. Luke hears
the humming sound. He presses a finger against
the side of his head. She turns back and watches
him for a moment.*

MUM Your dad used to do that. Touch his head
when he was hearing something unusual.
You're so like him. You even hear the same
sounds.   35

LUKE How do you know about the sounds I can hear?

MUM Your dad told me.

LUKE I never told him.

The sound begins to build.

MUM You didn't need to. He could tell. I'd wake up in
the night and he'd be lying there, eyes   40
closed, dead still but awake. And I'd ask him
what he was hearing and he'd say bells or
strings or buzzing or rushing water. Or
sometimes he'd hear complete pieces of
music, some of them pieces he'd never   45
heard before. But most often, it was a kind
of humming or roaring sound. He said that
sound was all the other sounds added

together. He called it the engine. He said it
was the engine that started creation and   50
keeps things running. But he didn't like
telling people about the sounds. He only
ever really told me and Mr Harding. He said
the sounds were sacred, and if he talked too
much, he thought they might leave him.   55

LUKE   I don't like talking about it either. But not
because of that, just because I don't want
people thinking I'm off my head.

Mum smiles. The sound dies away. Pause.

MUM   I'll tell you one thing he said. One night, I
found him at the kitchen table with some   60
paper and some crayons. He was cradling
you in his left arm and he was drawing a
picture. And he was crying.

LUKE   Dad was crying?

MUM   Tears pouring down his face. He said he   65
was as happy as he'd ever been. And then
he said, 'The firmament is singing.'

LUKE   What does that mean?

MUM   The firmament? It means the sky and
everything in it. The sun, the moon, the   70
stars. And it kind of means heaven as well.

LUKE   What was the picture of?

MUM   It was a picture of the sounds in his head. He
said he could draw sounds because sounds
have colours and shapes—   75

LUKE   But the picture. It was a five-pointed star,
wasn't it?

MUM *(amazed but not shocked)* Yeah. *(Pause)* He'd say everything in creation had a song of its own and, if you listened hard, you could hear   80
them.

LUKE Can we stop now?

Mum smiles sympathetically.

MUM Okay.

Mum moves to leave the kitchen.

LUKE Mum, this thing with Roger …

MUM It's over.   85

LUKE Completely?

MUM Completely. It's just you and me now.

Mum goes. Luke opens the laptop. He is surprised to find Mum's email account open.

LUKE Inbox. Roger Gillmore.

He gives in to temptation. Click. Roger appears.

ROGER Don't be sorry, Kirsti. I know you're hurting too. I understand that Luke comes first.   90

Pause. Click. Roger disappears.

LUKE New message. *(Click)* To admin@priory9.sch.uk. Dear Mrs Jay, I'm sorry but Luke is still ill so I've decided to keep him home another day. Kirsti Stanton. Send. *(Click)*

*   *   *

Recorded music plays: 'Peace Of The Forest'.

57

Scene 4

*Luke is playing 'Peace Of The Forest' for Natalie,
who is sitting on the floor. Mrs Little stands
nearby. After a short while, Natalie speaks ...*

NATALIE   Trees.

LUKE   *(continuing to play)* Trees? Is that what you can
see?

NATALIE   And leaves.

LUKE   You're like me. I see music too.   5

NATALIE   Sunshine.

*Luke finishes the piece. He looks through a book
of sheet music for something new to play ...*

LUKE   So she can remember things she's seen, from
before the accident?

LITTLE   Some things, yes. But I don't know how much.

LUKE   Does she know my name?   10

LITTLE   I've told her it but I don't suppose she took it
in.

LUKE   Do you know my name, Natalie?

NATALIE   Funny ears.

LUKE   Oh, is that my name? I thought my name   15
was Luke.

LITTLE   She'd be more likely to remember if you didn't
leave it so long between visits.

LUKE   I was here yesterday morning.

LITTLE   It was yesterday afternoon she needed you.   20
She was all right for a couple of hours after
you went, but then the crying started. It took

all day to calm her down. *(Pause)* If I make some tea, will you stay to drink it this time?

LUKE   Thanks.   25

Mrs Little goes. Luke turns away from the piano.

LUKE   What else can you remember from before the accident? *(Pause)* Can you remember where you lived? The name of the village?

He sits with her on the floor.

LUKE   Can you remember your second name? Or if you had any brothers or sisters? *(Pause)* No?   30
(Pause) Shall I play some more?

Luke moves to play the piano but Natalie clings tight to him and squeals.

LUKE   Hey, it's all right, it's okay, I'm not going anywhere. We can keep talking if you like.

Natalie hums the first six notes of 'Rêverie' but it is slurred and unrecognisable.

LUKE   What's that? Are you singing to me?

She sings again. This time, Luke recognises the tune. Pause.

LUKE   Sing that again for me.   35

She sings again. It is clearer still.

LUKE   I know that tune. I think about that tune a lot. Normally when I think about you.

Luke sings the notes back to her. Natalie repeats them.

LUKE	That tune, what's it called?
NATALIE	Bar-ley.
LUKE	Barley?	40
NATALIE	Barley.
LUKE	Is that what you see when you hear it? I can see a star. An amazing five-pointed star.

He sings the notes again. She starts to cry.

NATALIE	Barley, Barley!
LUKE	It's all right.	45
NATALIE	Barley!
LUKE	It's all right, I can see it too now. A field of barley swaying in the breeze. That's what I can see. It's all right, don't be sad.
NATALIE	Barley!	50

She goes. He calls after her.

| LUKE | Don't go, it's all right … |

Scene ends.

*   *   *

Luke's head is invaded by a growing noise: a disjointed music of horns, bells and flutes; a piercing whistle like an old fashioned kettle; wood being chopped; the hum and the roar. The noise continues into Scene 5 …

Scene 5

Mr Harding's room.

| HARDING | What's the matter? |

LUKE   I can hear sounds. Everywhere.

HARDING   I know you can.

LUKE   Can you hear them?

HARDING   No.   5

LUKE   It's not horrible.

HARDING   I know.

LUKE   It's just weird.

The sound reaches a climax and disappears.

LUKE   Mum told me Dad heard the same things. Like
           the jumble of instruments. And the roar. She   10
           said he talked to you about it.

HARDING   He did. He said it was the primal force that
           drives the cosmos and everything that exists.

LUKE   How though?

HARDING   Through vibration. All matter is in a constant 15
           state of vibration. Or, as your dad would put
           it, every stick, stone, cloud, animal or person
           has its own unique song, and that's what
           you're hearing. And he'd say thoughts have
           vibrations too, and feelings and desires. He'd   20
           say he could hear love or anger. And other
           sounds too, of forces and ideas beyond
           human imagination.

LUKE   I don't really understand.

HARDING   I think you understand better than you   25
           realise. You certainly understand better than
           I ever could. You hear the sounds, I never
           will.

LUKE   But you believe in them.

61

| HARDING | Only because I heard your dad speak about them. *(Pause)* Your dad, Luke, was an extraordinary man. He was just the same as you. Just as sensitive, just as easily hurt, just as musical— | 30 |

| LUKE | More musical. | 35 |

| HARDING | No, about the same, I'd say. And he'd agree. *(Pause)* Do you see things too? Do sounds have colours and shapes? |

| LUKE | Sometimes. |

| HARDING | *(plays a B flat on the piano)* B flat. What colour do you see? | 40 |

| LUKE | Green? |

| HARDING | *(plays a B major chord)* And what's that? |

| LUKE | It's a B major chord. |

| HARDING | What colour? | 45 |

| LUKE | Bright red. B flat major I get a mixture. Like bits of blue and bits of yellow. Did my dad see colours too? |

| HARDING | I think he did. Maybe not the same colours, but who knows? | 50 |

Pause.

| LUKE | Mr Harding, there was one other thing. |

| HARDING | Yes? |

| LUKE | A tune. I can't figure out what it is. |

| HARDING | Play the melody for me. |

| LUKE | It's been haunting me. | 55 |

Luke plays the first few notes of 'Rêverie'.

HARDING	Again.

He plays them again.

HARDING	That's 'Douce Rêverie' by Tchaikovsky.
LUKE	Have you got it?
HARDING	I think so.

Mr Harding searches for the music.

HARDING	And what colour is 'Douce Rêverie', Luke?	60
LUKE	It's deep blue. Like the sea.	
HARDING	And what else?	
LUKE	Gold? With a speck of light in the centre.	
HARDING	Just a speck of light? Not a star? *(Pause)* Your dad saw it too.	65
LUKE	What is it?	
HARDING	I asked him the same question. He said it was a symbol of the primal sound. And the gateway to another world.	

He gives Luke the music.

Scene 6

Natalie is crying.

∗   ∗   ∗

The crying continues as the phone begins to ring in Luke's kitchen. Luke comes into the kitchen, still holding the sheet music from Mr Harding, and picks up the phone. Mrs Little appears.

LUKE	Hello?

LITTLE   Luke. You need to come over.

LUKE   What?

LITTLE   You heard me.

LUKE   I've only just got in.   5

LITTLE   I don't care. She needs you.

LUKE   But—

LITTLE   It's never been this bad. Can you hear her?

LUKE   I've been hearing her all day.

LITTLE   What do you mean?   10

LUKE   Nothing.

LITTLE   Just hurry up. She needs you.

> *Mrs Little disappears. Luke hangs up and goes,*
> *taking the sheet music with him. The crying stops*
> *abruptly.*

                    *   *   *

> *Luke is walking over the bridge that passes over*
> *the brook. He drops the sheet music. As he*
> *gathers it up, Skin appears on the grass beneath.*
> *Daz follows shortly after. Luke listens to their*
> *conversation.*

DAZ   See. I told you he wouldn't be here.

SKIN   No you didn't.

DAZ   I said, 'He won't be by the brook, it's too   15
obvious'.

SKIN   Shut up, Daz.

DAZ   He's out-thinking you, Skin.

SKIN   What?!

DAZ   Nothing. Sorry, Skin.   20

       Pause.

SKIN   He's like a little worm, he keeps slipping
       through my fingers—

       Daz laughs loudly.

SKIN   What are you laughing at?

DAZ   Worm!

       Daz sees that Skin is unimpressed and falls silent.

DAZ   So what are you going to do, Skin?   25

SKIN   When?

DAZ   When we find him. Going to give him a good
       kicking?

SKIN   No. I've got way more interesting plans than
       that.   30

DAZ   Yeah?

SKIN   Yeah. I'm planning something big. Come on.

       *Daz and Skin move on. Luke finishes gathering his
       sheet music and continues on his way to Mrs
       Little's house.*

                    *   *   *

       *Natalie is at the piano, thumping the keys and
       crying. Mrs Little, herself in a state of some
       distress, leads Luke into the room.*

LITTLE She won't eat, she won't sleep, she just keeps
       crying. Natalie, it's Luke, he'll play for you.

LUKE   I'll play for you, shall I, Natalie? I've got   35
       some music I think you might like.

Luke hurriedly props the sheet music on the piano and begins to play 'Rêverie'. The effect on Natalie is almost instant. She stops crying.

LUKE   There. That's better, isn't it? You like this one, don't you?

The effect of the music on Natalie is almost hypnotic. She sits on the floor to listen. Before long, she is curled in a ball on the floor, asleep. Mrs Little sits. The music comes to an end. Luke turns and looks at Natalie.

LITTLE   Thank you.

LUKE   That's all right.   40

LITTLE   It's the worst she's been. If you hadn't come, I don't know what I would have done.

LUKE   Do you want me to carry her upstairs?

LITTLE   Would you?

Luke picks Natalie up.

LUKE   Come on, you need some sleep.   45

LITTLE   Put her in my bed for now.

LUKE   You look pretty tired as well.

LITTLE   I'll rest down here.

Luke takes Natalie up the stairs to Mrs Little's bedroom. He carefully puts her into bed and tucks her in.

LUKE   Get some sleep, eh?

He is about to leave the room when he sees Mrs Little's black velvet box. Silently, furtively, he

*walks across to the box and opens it. He takes out
a framed photograph and studies it. He puts the
photograph down and takes out a letter. Squadron
Leader James P Hutchinson appears.*

HUTCHINS Dear Mrs Little, it is with great regret that I   50
write to inform you that Bill was shot down
earlier today by enemy aircraft. I am sorry to
say there is no possibility that he could have
survived. It grieves me immensely to be the
bearer of such dreadful news. Bill was a   55
wonderful man, greatly respected by all of us
here, and he will be sorely missed. I enclose
a framed photograph of you both that was
found among his things. The rest of his
effects will, of course, be sent to you. Once   60
again, I am so sorry to have to give you such
shattering news. Yours sincerely, Squadron
Leader James P Hutchinson.

*Luke puts the letter on the table. He sees
something else in the box – an identity bracelet.*

LUKE *(reads from the bracelet)* 'Barley May Roberts.'

Mrs Little stands and heads upstairs.

LUKE 'Barley May Roberts.'   65

Mrs Little is not far from the bedroom …

LITTLE Luke.

*Luke hurriedly puts the letter and the picture back
in the box. He pockets the bracelet a second
before Mrs Little comes into the room.*

LITTLE Is everything all right?

Pause.

LUKE   Yeah.

Pause.

LITTLE   Good. You can go then, if you want to.

Scene 7

Night. Luke sits at the kitchen table. The laptop is closed in front of him. He stares at the bracelet. He closes his eyes and takes some deep breaths.

LUKE   I know you're there, Dad. I can feel you there. I'm just trying to do the best thing. You know that, don't you?

He opens his eyes and opens the laptop.

LUKE   Search. *(Click. Types ...)* Barley May Roberts. *(Click)* 'Barley May Roberts Official Website.'   5
         (Click)

Mrs Roberts appears.

MRS R   We haven't seen our beautiful daughter, Barley May Roberts, for two years now. She went missing on a trip to St Peter's park, outside Hastings, on June 17th 2005. Our attention was distracted away from her for   10
         just a few seconds, and in that time she disappeared. Now ten years old, Barley is a friendly and trusting girl. She was born with a learning disability and she attended Rose Hill Special School. Here is a photo of   15
         Barley taken shortly before her disappearance.

LUKE   Natalie …

MRS R   Please, if you have any information, call the
number below.   20

*Luke picks up the phone and dials the number. We
hear the phone ring several times, and then a
connection …*

MRS R   Hello? *(Pause)* Hello? *(Pause)* Fine, if you're
not going to speak—

LUKE   Wait!

Pause.

MRS R   Who is this? *(Pause)* If you've got something
to say, then say it. If you're a hoax caller,   25
you're certainly not the first. *(Pause)* Okay—

LUKE   No, wait, are you Mrs Roberts?

MRS R   Who is this?

LUKE   It's about Barley. I know where she is, and this
isn't a hoax, so just listen, all right?   30

MRS R   Where is she?

LUKE   She's safe. I promise, I've seen her—

MRS R   But where is she?

LUKE   Mrs Roberts, does Barley have any
grandparents?   35

MRS R   No, why? *(Pause)* Listen, whoever you are,
she's our daughter—

LUKE   I know that, and I'm going to help, you just
have to listen, all right? Hear me out.

Mr Roberts appears.

MR R	Who is it?	40
MRS R	It's about Barley.	
LUKE	Mrs Roberts, you've got to do what I say, all right? Okay, did you know … because it doesn't say anything on the website … When you last saw Barley, was she blind?	45
MRS R	She's blind?!	
MR R	What have you done to her?!	
LUKE	Nothing!	
MR R	Who the hell are you?!	
MRS R	Stop it—	50
MR R	What have you done?!	
MRS R	Please—	
LUKE	I haven't done anything!	
MR R	If you've hurt her, I will find you, I will find you!	55
LUKE	Stop it, I'm trying to help!	

Pause.

MRS R	Are you still there?	
LUKE	Yes.	
MRS R	You have to understand … We're in a terrible state over this, and we've had so many false alarms, and now you're telling us that she's blind …	60
LUKE	I know, I'm sorry. *(Pause)* But I promise you, this isn't a false alarm, I'll describe her to you. She's got—	65

MRS R	There's a photo on the website. How do we know that you're not just describing the photo?
LUKE	All right, I'll hum you a tune. Do you recognise this tune? 70

Luke hums 'Rêverie'. Mrs Roberts breaks down.

MR R	What's he doing?
MRS R	He's humming the tune.
MR R	What tune?
MRS R	'Rêverie'.

Luke stops humming.

MR R	Just tell us what we have to do. 75

Scene 8

Mrs Little's house. Barley is on the floor, sobbing. Luke has just arrived at the house.

LITTLE	I didn't expect you until late this afternoon. Aren't you supposed to be at school?
LUKE	I didn't go.
LITTLE	Won't you get in trouble?
LUKE	Probably. How did she sleep? 5
LITTLE	She slept right through after you left. But then she woke up around five and started with all this moaning and weeping. She hasn't stopped since.

Luke crouches by Barley and strokes her hair.

LUKE	Hi, Natalie. Remember me? 10

She clings to Luke. She holds his ears.

LUKE That's right. Funny ears.

He hums 'Rêverie' to Barley. She stops crying.

LUKE Good girl. No more tears.

LITTLE You obviously have the magic touch.

LUKE Yeah.

Pause, Luke stroking Barley's hair.

LUKE Mrs Little …   15

LITTLE Yes?

LUKE Could I have a drink, please?

LITTLE I'll get you some orange juice.

LUKE Yeah, could I have something hot? Anything
       will do. Cup of tea, hot chocolate, whatever.   20

Pause.

LITTLE I'll make some hot chocolate. Natalie likes hot
        chocolate.

LUKE With lots of sugar, please.

Pause.

LITTLE How many spoonfuls?

LUKE What?   25

LITTLE I told you, I don't like it when you say what.

LUKE Sorry.

LITTLE How many spoonfuls of sugar?

LUKE Two, please.

Mrs Little goes. Silently, Luke picks Barley up.

LUKE *(whispers)* Quiet now, Barley. I'm taking you 30
      home.

      *Luke checks that it is safe to go and leaves with
      Barley.*

                  *   *   *

      Luke is carrying Barley through the forest.

LUKE You okay, Barley?

BARLEY Trees.

LUKE Can you hear the trees?

BARLEY Hear the trees … 35

LUKE We're going to stop here, okay?

      Luke stops and puts Barley down.

BARLEY Barley.

LUKE That's right. That's your name, isn't it? Barley
      May Roberts. I'm just going to make a phone
      call, okay? 40

      *Luke takes out a mobile phone and dials. Mr and
      Mrs Roberts appear.*

MRS R Yes?

LUKE It's me. Are you in Bramblebury yet?

MRS R Yes. We're by a thatched cottage with a white
      gate.

LUKE Good. Head north along that road. 45

MRS R Towards Upper Dinton?

LUKE That's it. You'll be driving along the edge of
      Buckland Forest. After a while there'll be a

layby on your left. It's by a field with loads of
buttercups in it. Pull in there and wait.   50

MRS R   And then you'll phone?

LUKE   Yes.

MRS R   But you will phone, won't you?

LUKE   Yes, I'll phone. I promise you, Mrs Roberts,
        you'll have Barley back very soon.   55

*Mr and Mrs Roberts disappear. Luke goes back to
Barley. He strokes her hair.*

LUKE   Only me. Are you all right?

BARLEY Singing.

LUKE   Who's singing?

BARLEY Trees.

LUKE   The trees are singing. I think you're right.   60
        There's lots of different trees around here, all
        singing different songs. There's a tree over
        there that's mine.

He points Barley's arm in the direction of his tree.

        Me and my dad put a tree-house in it. *(Pause)*
        Now listen, Barley. I want you to know that   65
        I'll always be thinking about you, and I'll
        always love you. And so will Nana. And
        mummy and daddy will always love you too.
        They're going to be here very soon, okay?
        And they're going to look after you again.   70

Luke begins to hum 'Rêverie'. Barley joins in.

LUKE   That's it. Keep humming. I'm just going over
        here for a while. Keep humming.

Barley keeps humming. Luke dials. Mr and Mrs Roberts appear.

LUKE   Mrs Roberts.

MRS R   Yes?

LUKE   Okay. Get out of the car.   75

MRS R   Yes.

LUKE   And cross the road.

MR R   What's he saying?

MRS R   Cross the road.

LUKE   Can you see a path into the forest?   80

MRS R   Yes.

LUKE   Go down there. *(Pause)* Are you on the path?

MRS R   Yes.

LUKE   Keep walking. *(Pause)* Keep walking. *(Pause)*
         Okay, I'm going to go now—   85

MRS R   No, don't go—

LUKE   I have to go, but keep walking and very soon
         you'll see her. But please don't rush and
         don't call out, okay? Goodbye.

Luke hangs up. Pause.

MR R   Barley?   90

*Mr and Mrs Roberts slowly approach Barley, being
careful not to frighten her. They are drained but
elated. They kneel with her and hold her. Luke
looks on from behind a tree. They take her away.
A happy, warm, exhilarating noise begins to
emanate from the trees.*

LUKE The trees are singing.

The noise builds. It is coming from everywhere now, especially the sky. Luke looks up in wonder.

LUKE The firmament is singing.

*   *   *

The sound continues as Skin and Daz arrive, unseen by Luke. Daz grabs Luke from behind and turns him round to face Skin, holding his arms, restricting his movement.

SKIN Thought we were in school, did you?

LUKE Skin—

SKIN Well, you got that wrong, didn't you?   95

Skin grabs Luke's face.

SKIN Stupid thing is, Luke, none of this needed to happen, did it? You only had to do what we agreed. But you went and let us down, didn't you? And then you stopped showing respect. And that's not something we ever forgive.   100

Skin takes a cigarette lighter out and snaps it open. A big flame. He waves it close to Luke's face.

DAZ Skin …

SKIN What?

DAZ I reckon he's learnt his lesson.

SKIN Well, I don't.

DAZ Come on …   105

SKIN Just shut up and hold him or I'll do you an' all!

Daz holds Luke. Skin slowly runs the flame down Luke's arm.

SKIN   I told you, Luke. I told you what would happen if you messed with me. I warned you and you can't say I didn't.

Skin takes hold of one of Luke's hands. He teases it with the flame.

SKIN   That's the thing with piano players, I   110
suppose. Need a good pair of hands. Your hands insured, Lukey?

Luke says nothing.

SKIN   Oh, that's a shame, cos after today you won't be playing piano again. In fact, you ain't going to be doing anything. That's right—   115

DAZ   Skin, listen—

SKIN   Shut up, Daz.

DAZ   But do we have to?

SKIN   Shut up, I said! We agreed!

Skin starts to burn Luke's hand. Luke struggles.

SKIN   Such pretty hands. I bet your dad had   120
pretty hands.

Luke pulls free of Daz. Skin tries to grab him but Luke wrestles free, pushing Skin to the ground. Luke runs off.

SKIN   Well, don't just stand there!

DAZ   Eh?

SKIN   Go on!

They chase him.

*   *   *

Luke is climbing the tree. Skin arrives just too late as Luke pulls himself beyond his reach, apparently to safety. He reaches his tree-house.

SKIN   Don't think you're going to be safe up there.   125
Because you're not. This is the day you're
going to die.

Daz arrives.

SKIN   Come on, Daz, get to work.

*Daz starts to bring tyres and branches from a
hiding place nearby. He heaps them around the
foot of the tree.*

SKIN   We thought you might try something like this
so we made a few preparations. So, you   130
might as well sit back and relax, Luke. Enjoy
your last few moments on earth.

Luke takes out his mobile and dials.

LUKE   Mum, I'm in trouble—

SKIN   Ahh, he's phoning his mum—

LUKE   If you get this message—   135

SKIN   Bless!

LUKE   I'm in the forest, in my tree, Skin's going to kill
me, don't come on your own.

Luke dials a different number.

SKIN   That's the stuff, Daz. Pile it nice and high. This
is going to be fun, don't you reckon, Luke?   140

LUKE   Roger, it's Luke, I'm in trouble, I'm in the tree-
        house, please come and help.

SKIN   All right, Daz, that'll do. Now, get the diesel.

DAZ   Skin—

SKIN   Get it!   145

        Daz fetches a can of diesel. Skin takes if off him.
        He pours it on the tyres and branches around the
        tree.

SKIN   What we have here, Luke, is diesel. Specially for
        you. And with these tyres it's going to make
        quite a lot of thick, black smoke. Not very
        nice to breathe in. Going to finish you off, it
        is. And your precious tree. I warned you,   150
        Luke.

        Daz runs off.

SKIN   I warned you!

        Skin holds the lighter to the diesel …

LUKE   No …

        Skin sets light to the tree and runs off after Daz.

LUKE   No …!

        The fire builds quickly, cracking and roaring. Thick
        smoke billows from it.

LUKE   Help! Somebody please! Help me! Help!   155
        Anyone! Please!

        Luke begins to cough.

LUKE   Help! Help!

He wipes the tears from his eyes and the spit from his mouth.

LUKE   Smoke.
        Black smoke and so much of it.
        My eyes are burning,   160
        My lungs are like fists,
        My mouth is … aching for air!

The roar of the fire becomes deafening, drowning Luke out. It reaches a powerful crescendo and Luke suddenly finds himself at the centre of an entirely different, altogether woozier world of unfamiliar, muffled, heavenly noise.

LUKE   I'm falling.
        But at the same time going up.
        Flying up through my tree,   165
        Past the branches,
        Through the leaves,
        Out into the sky.
        I can breathe up here.
        I can breathe.   170
        And I can see my own body
        Sprawled out on the ground.

A blissful light shines on Luke, growing brighter and brighter.

LUKE   There's a star up above me and it speaks:
        'Are you ready to die?
        Or are you ready to live?'   175

The world becomes silent.

LUKE   I think of Mum.
        And Miranda.

And Mrs Little
And Barley
And Mr Harding.   180
And I think of Dad.
I'm ready to live.

The deafening noise returns ...

LUKE   I'm ready to live!

*Luke is plunged into darkness but the noise
continues, roaring, rattling and crackling to a
climax.*

Scene 9

*A hospital room. Luke is asleep in a hospital bed.
Roger is by the bed, his arm in a sling. Luke wakes
up. Moving and speaking is painful for him.*

LUKE   Roger. Where am I?

ROGER   In hospital.

LUKE   *(tries to sit up)* Eh?

ROGER   Take it easy, you're not in a good way.

LUKE   What happened?   5

ROGER   Don't you remember?

Luke thinks.

LUKE   I remember being stuck up the tree. And all the
smoke. And I kind of remember … lying on
the ground, talking to you.

ROGER   That's right, we were waiting for the   10
ambulance.

LUKE   Yeah. You looked after me. How did you get hurt?

ROGER   Me? Don't worry about me. Just a couple of scratches. It's you we've all been worried about.   15

LUKE   Yeah … Thanks, Roger.

Mum comes into the room.

MUM   You're awake.

LUKE   Hello, Mum.

MUM   How are you feeling?   20

LUKE   I've felt better.

MUM   I'm not surprised.

ROGER   I'll leave you two alone, shall I?

LUKE   Stay.

ROGER   No, I'll go, I'll be back in a bit.   25

Roger goes. Pause.

MUM   Silly boy.

LUKE   I phoned you, didn't I? When I was in the tree-house.

MUM   I was on the phone to Mrs Jay. She was asking me when you'd be well enough to come back 30 to school.

LUKE   Sorry.

MUM   It doesn't matter now.

LUKE   What happened? I can remember … like a figure running forward as I fell …   35

MUM   That was Roger. He got your message and ran down just in time to see you falling. He got underneath you to cushion your fall.

LUKE   Must have hurt.

MUM   I think it did, he broke his wrist and put his 40
shoulder out. And then he had to drag you away from the smoke, by which time you'd stopped breathing, so he gave you CPR. He saved your life.

LUKE   I always said he was a nice bloke. 45

Mum smiles.

LUKE   Who called the ambulance?

MUM   Darren Fisher. It seems like he had an attack of conscience.

Pause.

LUKE   I'm so sorry, Mum.

MUM   It's all right. 50

LUKE   I'll make things better, I promise.

MUM   It's okay. There's nothing broken that can't be fixed.

LUKE   I will, I'll make it all better. *(Pause)* You'd better marry him after all this. What else has a 55
bloke got to do?

Mum smiles.

Scene 10

Luke sits at the piano. He splays his fingers in the air. He winces with pain as the skin on his burnt hand stretches. He begins to play the incomplete piece from Act One, Scene 5. The music runs out at the same point as before. Pause. Luke's dad appears. He joins Luke at the piano. He plays three notes. Luke uses these three notes to take the piece beyond its normal stopping point. The music continues for a few seconds before breaking down again. Again, Luke's dad provides a new direction for the music, playing three more notes for Luke to use. It is as if Luke's dad is both a part of him and separate from him. He stimulates Luke's imagination, and yet at the same time he is Luke's imagination.

*   *   *

Outside Luke's house. Mrs Little is standing in the road. She looks somehow older and more frail than before. Luke stands opposite her.

LITTLE   The police called yesterday. I'd been expecting them.

LUKE   I didn't tell them anything. About you and Barley.

LITTLE   It wasn't about that. They came to see me   5
about you. One of your friends, Jason—

LUKE   I told you, he's not my friend.

LITTLE   Well, that's good, because it seems he's on his
way to an institute for young offenders. He
told the police you broke into my house to   10
steal a jewellery box.

LUKE   And what did you say?

LITTLE   I said you'd come to my house to play the piano
a few times, but that I was certain you never

had any intention to steal from me. A lie, of 15
course. You stole a bracelet. You also read a
private letter.

LUKE   Sorry.

LITTLE   A letter you had no right to read.

LUKE   So why didn't you give me away? 20

LITTLE   Because you didn't give me away. *(Pause)* All
I ever wanted, apart from Bill, was a child.
When I opened that letter, those dreams
died. I knew I'd never love another man, and
what man would love me? 25

LUKE   Bill loved you.

LITTLE   Bill was different. *(Pause)* Not everything I said
was a lie.

LUKE   So what really happened?

LITTLE   I was driving back from my brother's funeral 30
and I saw her in a ditch. She was bleeding
from the head. She'd been hit by a car. I was
driving her to a phone box to call for an
ambulance … and she reached out a hand to
me. And it was like meeting our child, the 35
child Bill and I never had.

LUKE   But she wasn't yours.

LITTLE   I know that. I felt guilty. But I felt … I feel …
like I was meant to find her.

LUKE   But not to keep her. What about her parents? 40

LITTLE   They let her go.

LUKE   They took their eyes off her for two seconds.

LITTLE   If they can't take proper care of her—

LUKE   That's rubbish and you know it.

Pause.

LITTLE   I should have got her back to them. I know   45
that. But she seemed happy at first. Who
knows, if she'd never heard the piano, she
might have stayed that way. *(Pause)* What I
did was wrong. *(Pause)* You asked me once
why I keep a piano if I don't play. Bill used   50
to play. I keep it for Bill.

Pause.

LUKE   I'm playing a concert tonight. At the village hall.
I think you should come.

LITTLE   I don't think so.

Mrs Little walks away.

Scene 11

*Luke and Miranda play the last minute of 'Dance of
the Blessed Spirits'. As they finish, and the crowd
applauds, Mr Harding steps forward ...*

HARDING   Ladies and gentlemen, that was Miranda Davis
playing Gluck's 'Dance of the Blessed Spirits',
accompanied by Luke Stanton on piano.
Congratulations Miranda.

*More applause. Luke walks away from the concert.
Miranda follows him.*

MIRANDA   Luke, where are you going?   5

LUKE   I need to be somewhere.

MIRANDA   What do you mean?

LUKE   The forest. I need to go back.

MIRANDA	Why?	
LUKE	I don't know, I can't explain—	10
MIRANDA	You haven't played your piece yet.	
LUKE	I'll be back in time. It's just something I've got to do, all right?	
MIRANDA	Okay.	

Luke walks away.

MIRANDA	Luke.	15
LUKE	Yeah?	
MIRANDA	Can I come too? I'm worried about you.	

Pause.

LUKE	Yeah. I'd like that.

*　　　*　　　*

Luke and Miranda are in the forest. They arrive at the charred oak tree.

MIRANDA	It's your tree.	
LUKE	Not my tree.	20
MIRANDA	I think of it as your tree.	

Luke hears a strange sound, like a musical sigh.

MIRANDA	Luke? Are you all right?

He hears the sound again.

MIRANDA	What's wrong?	
LUKE	Nothing. But do you mind if …?	
MIRANDA	You want to be on your own.	25
LUKE	Sorry.	

MIRANDA   Don't be sorry, I understand.

LUKE   Thanks.

MIRANDA   I'll just wait over there.

LUKE   Thanks, Miranda. Are you going to be all right? 30

MIRANDA   Of course. Just shout if you need me.

Miranda goes. Luke turns to look at the tree. He hears the noise again as his dad appears from behind the tree. Dad smiles. Luke slowly moves towards his dad until their faces are almost touching. A moment of stillness and peace.

LUKE   It's okay. I'm going to be all right.

Luke opens his arms but his dad moves calmly away. Luke is left alone, his arms empty, outstretched.

LUKE   Dad?

Pause.

LUKE   Dad?!

Miranda comes back.

MIRANDA   Luke? Are you all right?   35

He turns to see her, his arms still open. She mirrors the gesture. They hold each other and he starts to cry.

MIRANDA   It's okay. It's okay.

LUKE   Don't let go of me.

MIRANDA   I won't. Don't let go of me.

LUKE   I won't.

*They kiss, Luke still crying. As they kiss, beautiful
sound engulfs Luke: the sound of the forest; the
sound of Barley, Mrs Little, Mum, Roger and
everyone he ever met; the sound of Dad; the
sound of music he has heard and music that is yet
to come; the sound of 'the engine'. The kiss ends.
The sounds fade, leaving only 'the engine'
humming quietly.*

MIRANDA   You're still crying. You're going to be okay.   40

LUKE   I know.

            Pause.

MIRANDA   Poor thing.

LUKE   Me?

MIRANDA   The tree.

LUKE   The tree's going to be okay.   45

MIRANDA   Roger thinks it's going to die.

LUKE   It won't. It's singing.

MIRANDA   What?

LUKE   I can hear it singing. It's woken up.

            Miranda smiles.

LUKE   Come on, we need to get back. I'm on in   50
            ten minutes.

*   *   *

*Back in the concert room. As Mr Harding
addresses the audience, Mrs Little slips into the
hall to listen.*

HARDING   And now we come to the final piece of the
            evening, which will be played, against his

doctor's wishes, by a young musician of quite exceptional talent whom it has been 55 my pleasure and my privilege to teach in recent years. He's playing a piece of his own choosing. In fact, even I don't know what we're about to hear and the suspense is killing me. So, without further ado, it's with 60 no small measure of pride that I give to you Luke Stanton playing a piece by …?

LUKE   Stanton.

HARDING   Stanton, and which Stanton is that?

LUKE   Both.   65

Luke plays the previously unfinished piece that he composed with his dad in Act Two, Scene 10. It is brilliant and is met with ecstatic applause.

Luke and his mum

Luke in his bedroom and Luke's dad playing the piano

Luke and Natalie/Barley

Skin, Luke and Daz

Mrs Little and Natalie/Barley

Luke hugging Natalie/Barley with Mrs Little in the background

Introduction to the Activities

The activities that follow will help you come to a greater understanding of the textual features and dramatic techniques in *Starseeker*. They explore the writing process and writer's techniques as well as the thematic, content-based issues and ideas. You will develop your analytical skills and ability to respond effectively to the play as well as your ability to apply this critical thinking to other texts, ideas or issues.

The group nature of the activities and the critical thinking skills you will develop demand that you explore and respond to the play both in relation to its staging and performance, as well as in relation to Tim Bowler's novel from which it has been adapted. Exploring and analysing the adaptation from novel to play allows you to examine the decisions, techniques and imagination required to move it from prose to script and from page to stage.

The activities offered here provide a structure that enables you to build your learning and understanding. You will collaborate in pairs and groups under the guidance of your teacher. It is important that you are aware of the learning process and understand the aims and objectives outlined at the start of each activity. Recording your thinking will help to inform the work and your written responses as they develop.

From the initial planning to the final staging of the play for an audience, the activities can become an important part of the performance process. An understanding of the writer's techniques and the adaptation and decision-making process has a direct impact on the way in which actors and non-actors approach a performance of the script. Just as influential is an appreciation of the roles of the writer, playwright, director and audience.

Although the approaches are related to specific scenes and aspects of the play, the conventions and techniques can clearly be used in relation to other aspects of the play and/or other texts. You will, throughout the work, develop your ability to analyse and respond to texts. You will also increase your understanding of drama conventions and develop the drama skills required to approach a variety of texts, issues or ideas.

Paul Bunyan and Ruth Moore

Activity 1: Sounds and images

Learning outcomes

You will:

- develop your understanding of image, sound and colour in the play
- question the ideas introduced at the beginning of the play
- develop the use of space.

You will do this by creating a **Still Image** in response to the opening lines of the play and music.

1 Sit in a large circle. Your teacher will give you a card showing a word (or words) from the opening lines of the play.

2 The class will read out all the words around the circle, creating the first few lines of the play. As you hear the words, think carefully about what they mean. Music will be played (the music composed by Luke and his father), which will continue once the reading has stopped.

3 What do you think these lines suggest about the character who says them? Why might they be important when studying the play?

4 Work in groups of three or four. In your groups, think carefully about the opening lines and music that you have listened to. Present a **Still Image** that you feel best illustrates your response to the text and music. The **Still Image** may be symbolic, using shapes and heights, or realistic through the use of frozen characters.

> **Still Image:** a Still Image is created by participants in the drama standing motionless, often at a given sign by the teacher or as a result of being sculpted by other students into the frozen image. This convention is used to mark a significant moment or enable time for reflection.

5   Decide what colour you would associate with the **Still Image** you
have created. Select a ribbon closest to the colour you have
chosen. Incorporate the ribbon into your **Still Image**. Is it wrapped
around particular people, laid randomly on the floor or used to
circle the group?

What have I learnt?

- What skills have you used/developed in this activity?
- What have you learnt about some of the issues that might be
explored in the play?
- How did choosing a **Still Image** and coloured ribbon help you to
think about the use of sound and colour in the play?

Activity 2: Introducing a character

Learning outcomes

You will:

- investigate a character and question the significance of her
possessions
- develop your understanding of colour and its significance in the
play
- develop your understanding of symbolism and props in the play
- listen to, organise and present ideas.

You will do this by observing and analysing the character's actions
and by selecting and placing objects associated with particular
colours.

1   Sit in a large circle. Your teacher will sit in the centre of the circle
with a box. In role, your teacher will gradually take some objects
out of the box, one by one. Music will be played while everyone
watches how the character reacts to the objects. As you are
watching the character, think about what significance the objects
might have.

2 Discuss why these objects might be kept in a box and what they might tell us about the person who owns the box. What have you witnessed?

3 With a partner, select one of the objects. Decide what colour you would associate with it. This might be in terms of how the owner felt at the time or the atmosphere that is created by it. Select a ribbon closest to the colour you have chosen.

4 You will be asked to bring the object out to the character with the box. As you do so, complete the following two lines:

> She remembers...
> I see the colour ... because...

You will also bring one end of the ribbon out with the object, leaving the other end of the ribbon where you were sitting. Music will be played while everyone in the circle completes this activity.

What have I learnt?
- What skills have you used/developed in this activity?
- What have you learnt about some of the ideas that might be explored in the play?
- How did choosing an object and colour help you to think about the use of symbolism and props in the play?

Activity 3a: Setting a context and introducing sounds

Learning outcomes

You will:

- analyse a picture
- investigate, in role, the context and setting of the play
- describe and explain accurately
- listen to and select information.

You will do this by exploring Mrs Little's house and feeding back what you have discovered about the place.

1   Sit in a large semi-circle facing the large projected image of the house.

2   Identify what you can see in the picture. First, describe what you actually see and then try to interpret the picture. What sort of place is it? What atmosphere is created?

3   In pairs, decide who is 'A' and who is 'B'.

4   As a class, you are divided into two groups. If you are student A, make sure you are looking at the picture as this is the place you are about to explore with your partner on a **Guided Tour**.

5   Student A: You need to imagine that you know the place very well. Using the picture, take your partner on a **Guided Tour**. Describe and comment on the things that are around him/her as you move around the space.

Student B: You need to close your eyes while your partner holds you by the arm and guides you around the space. Listen to his/ her description carefully as you will be asked later to feed back to the class what you have found out.

6   Your teacher will provide a few seconds of narration to introduce the place and will then ask you to begin the **Guided Tour**.

7   Listen to the music as you make your way around the place.

8   When you are asked to freeze, stop quickly and keep very still and silent.

Now it is time to feed back to the class. If you are Student B, describe to the class what you have seen in your 'drama eyes', heard in your 'drama ears' and perhaps smelled in your 'drama noses' as you were guided around the garden. Listen carefully to the information provided by the other students.

What have I learnt?

- What skills have you used/developed in this activity?
- How were you able to describe the place in such detail? What did you use to help you to do this?
- What have you learnt about the setting and context of the play?

Activity 3b: Developing the context and introducing text

Learning outcomes

You will:

- further investigate the context and setting of the play
- describe and explain accurately
- listen and think carefully about the text that you hear.

You will do this by continuing to explore the garden and being introduced to an extract from the play.

1   Reverse your roles from Activity 3a by swapping the tasks of A and B in your pair. This time, the Bs imagine that they know the place very well and take the As on a **Guided Tour**.

> **Guided Tour:** in pairs, A (with eyes open) leads B (with eyes closed) slowly through an imaginary environment while providing a spoken commentary. The environment or location may be based on text but will usually be stimulated by a printed or projected map or 'bird's-eye' picture. Roles can be reversed to enable all participants to share the experience.

2 Listen carefully to your teacher narrating information about the place using ideas from the feedback that you gave in Activity 3a. Remember that when you hear 'freeze' you must stop exactly where you are, stay completely still and listen to what is said.

3 Continue the **Guided Tour**. Student A, as well as listening carefully to the description and music, can now ask Student B questions about the place.

4 Freeze and think carefully about the description you have given or heard. As a pair, decide on an important word or phrase that you think best describes the atmosphere in the garden or a particular feature in it. When the teacher taps you on the shoulder, begin repeating the word or phrase in a way that creates a particular sound effect. Think about how you will say it: quickly or slowly, loudly or in a whisper, or in a varied tone? The teacher will walk around the room, tapping people on the shoulder. Those who have been 'tapped' will begin to say the words or phrases until a complete soundscape has been created with everyone saying their words and phrases.

5 When the teacher taps you on the shoulder again, stop speaking. Freeze and listen to the extract from page 8 of the play, following the text projected onto the screen.

A grey light picks out Mrs Little, an old and peculiar-looking woman, standing by a high window, looking out. She is holding a box. The box has a black velvet exterior, thick silver beading on its lid and a brocade tassel. From somewhere behind Mrs Little comes the sound of a girl crying. The sound is not piercing or harrowing, just a sad and steady, heartfelt cry.

Cradling the box with great tenderness, Mrs Little lifts its lid and looks inside. She has seen its contents many times before. To look at them brings both pain and relief. The light on Mrs Little becomes hotter and the girl's cry becomes just slightly more urgent. Mrs Little closes her eyes for a moment. She opens her eyes and closes the box gently. The light and the crying fade away.

What have I learnt?

- What else have you learnt about the setting and context of the play?
- By investigating the extract, what other information have you gained?
- Which issues or ideas do you think will be particularly significant in the play?
- How has the **Guided Tour** activity helped you to gain an understanding of the setting and enabled you to think about the context of the play?

Activity 4: Exploring the character of Mrs Little

Learning outcomes

You will:

- investigate the character of Mrs Little
- select appropriate information
- organise and present ideas
- analyse the way that colour has different meanings.

You will do this by analysing an extract from the play and making reasoned judgements about the information you are given.

1 As a class, return to the extract used by the teacher at the end of the **Guided Tour** activity (Activity 3b, pages 101–102).

2 Use the **Role on the Spectrum** convention to explore the character of Mrs Little. To do this, you need to identify from the extract what you know and select a word that you feel best describes her. Your teacher will write this word on a piece of card, which you then place onto a colour spectrum. Think carefully about where you might place the word according to the colour beneath it.

> **Role on the Spectrum:** to help define character traits at particular moments in drama, a colour spectrum is placed in front of the participants. Students place words about a character onto the colour spectrum, thinking carefully about the colour on which they place each word.

3 You will return to this **Role on the Spectrum** at different stages in the play by adding words and discussing your previous choices. You might also want use the same technique to record your responses, ideas and comments about the play as a whole. This will provide a useful prompt and recap tool and provide you with a valuable resource when you are planning your written responses to the text.

What have I learnt?

- What analytical skills have you developed in this activity?
- How did you decide what words to choose for Mrs Little? Do you think this description will remain throughout the whole play? Why?
- How does placing the words carefully on the different colours add to their meaning?
- How might this activity help with your understanding of the writer's use of colour, sounds and symbols in the play?

Activity 5: Introducing and investigating the play

Learning outcomes

You will:

- develop the use of space, facial expression, gesture and tone
- investigate and analyse the script
- question critically the ideas and issues introduced at the beginning of the play.

You will do this by investigating an extract and considering how the script might be staged in order to produce **Digital Video Clips.**

> **Digital Video Clip:** a short, repeatable dramatic sequence is 'bookended' with a **Still Image** at the start and a **Still Image** at the end.

1   You will be working in a group of three to five students. Each group is given an extract from Act One, Scene 1 (from page 8 'Luke stands at the bottom of a drainpipe' to page 12 'Skin: – Just as soon as I've taught you a lesson in respect').

2   In your group, produce a short **Digital Video Clip** of the extract. To do this, you begin with a **Still Image**, followed by an **Action Reading** of the script, and then freeze at the end in a final **Still Image**. You need to investigate the script and search for clues about the characters, story and setting in order to produce an accurate **Action Reading** of the extract.

> **Action Reading:** students, in role, walk through a scene, speaking lines and adding gestures and movements, while reading from scripts.

3 As a class, you produce your **Digital Video Clips** as **Rolling Theatre**. Music is used to guide you.

- All the groups freeze in their initial **Still Image**.
- The first group unfreezes, adds the action and then freezes again. When they freeze, the next group know that they can begin.
- This continues with each group producing their **Digital Video Clip**, until all groups have shown their pieces.

When you are not presenting your **Digital Video Clip**, you can become a **Spectactor**. This means that while your body remains frozen in the **Still Image**, your head can turn to follow the action so that you can see and hear the work of the other groups. However, you must remain in your place in order for all the groups to freeze in their final **Still Image** at the end.

Rolling Theatre: groups can share their work on different aspects of a drama, learning from each other by running several rehearsed sections in a sequence.

Spectactor: performers in a drama session can follow the action with their eyes and heads when the focus is not directly upon them.

Extracts

Extract 1: stage instruction before line 24 to line 35 (pages 8–9)

| *from* | | *Luke stands at the bottom of the drainpipe ...* |
| *to* | SKIN | *... I reckon she keeps it there —* |

Extract 2: line 36 to line 43 (page 9)

from	DAZ	Obsessed with that box...
to	SKIN	... She'll be back soon. (*Pause*) Oi!

Extract 3: stage instruction after line 43 to stage instruction on page 10 (pages 9–10)

from	*The sound of crying remains...*
to	*She begins to cry again as he runs down the stairs.*

Extract 4: stage instruction on page 10 to line 57 (pages 10–11)

from		*Luke is now climbing a large oak tree...*
to	SKIN	... You got to face us soon enough, Lukey Boy!

Extract 5: line 60 to 63 (page 11)

from	SKIN	Shut up, Daz.
to	LUKE	All right, Skin?

Extract 6: stage direction after line 63 to line 72 (pages 11–12)

from		*Luke thinks about making a run for it but Daz is behind him.*
to	DAZ	Whether you like it or not.

Extract 7: line 73 to line 79 (page 12)

from	SKIN	We're meeting tomorrow morning...
to	SKIN	Just as soon as I've taught you a lesson in respect.

4 Choose the most significant sentence from the extract and present this as a **Still Image**.

5 Your teacher will stand between two of the characters in a **Still Image**. Try to describe the space between the characters. You might suggest various alternatives: the space of hatred, fear, or loyalty.

What have I learnt?

- How did performing these extracts help you to gain an understanding of the issues, characters and setting?
- How did you use space, gestures, tone, pace and facial expressions during the **Digital Video Clip**?
- What have you learnt about the characters and events in the play?

Activity 6: Exploring tension – sculpting the scene and the characters

Learning outcomes

You will:

- explore the relationship between characters in the play
- explore the tension created
- use your understanding of the play so far to approach the activity with skill and integrity
- demonstrate an understanding of the drama process.

You will do this by sculpting the characters and using the **Communal Voice** convention to explore the tension in the play and the motivation of the characters.

> **Communal Voice:** individual members of the group take up positions, one at a time, behind a sculpted character and speak the words that the character says at a chosen moment in the drama.

1   Read the following extract from Scene 6 (pages 27–29):

| from | *Luke stands at the bottom of the drainpipe that runs down the side of Mrs Little's house...* |
| to | *... Luke sees the box on the other side of the room.* |

2 Props from Mrs Little's dressing table are laid randomly on a table. Place the props on another table exactly as you think they would be placed on Mrs Little's dressing table. This designated drama space in front of the table and the projected extract will become the 'set' in which the drama will take place. The teacher reads (page 29):

> *He moves silently across to it and picks it up.*

3 A member of the class is given the role of Luke. **Sculpt** him into the position you believe he will be in when the action takes place. He freezes as the teacher reads (page 29):

> *As he does so, Mrs Little appears behind him. She has a stick in one hand and a cordless phone in the other.*

Sculpting: participants offer suggestions while placing an individual in a significant, frozen position so that considered analysis can take place.

---

4 Another member of the class is given the role of Mrs Little. She is **sculpted** into the scene and freezes while your teacher re-reads (page 29):

> *As he does so, Mrs Little appears behind him. She has a stick in one hand and a cordless phone in the other.*

5 The remaining members of the class are asked who they think would speak first and what they would say. When one student suggests the next line to be spoken, the characters remain frozen while that student goes to stand behind the character they will speak for. The end of the extract is read again, at the end of which the student who is stood behind the character will say his/her suggested line. The remaining members of the class are then asked what they think the characters would say next. Individual students go and stand by the character they think they can speak for.

6 The scene is frozen again. One by one the students behind the **sculpted** characters will continue the scene by speaking what the characters say or think. Using **Communal Voice**, continue the conversation between Luke and Mrs Little, remembering that at times there may be silences. The voices may then be stripped away and the two **sculpted** characters continue the conversation until the teacher freezes the action.

What have I learnt?

- How does this activity help you to explore the tensions that exist in the play?
- What techniques has the playwright used to develop the tension?
- What helped you to decide what the characters would say? What skills did you need?

Activity 7: Luke's conscience

Learning outcomes

You will:

- continue to explore and analyse the tension in the play
- make reasoned judgements and organise and present your ideas
- investigate and analyse the text to identify the character's thoughts and motivation.

You will do this by using the **Conscience Alley** convention to explore the tension in the scene and the motivation of the character.

Conscience Alley: the group is divided into two lines facing each other. A student (or teacher) in role as a character in the drama walks between the two lines as individuals speak out what is in the character's conscience. Each line might represent opposing perspectives.

1   The teacher will read the text as Mrs Little asks for Luke's help
    (lines 47–94, pages 30–32):

    from   LITTLE   I've been hearing a lot about you and your
                          gang.
    to   LITTLE   (*to Luke. Cold*) Please come back.

    Face the large projected image of the tree.

2   Standing in two parallel lines, facing each other, you represent the
    branches that Luke has to climb to get to his space where he can
    make a decision. Your teacher will stand in between these lines at
    one end of the room, looking down the lines towards the
    projected tree.

3   The teacher will adopt the role of Luke. As he walks down in
    between the two lines, he will hear his conscience speaking to
    him. One line of students will speak Luke's negative thoughts as
    he struggles against the branches to reach his decision. The other
    line of students will speak his positive thoughts as the branches
    help him to climb towards a positive solution.

4   As he becomes level with you, you will speak his thoughts. Think
    carefully about the text you have just explored and what you feel
    are the character's motivations. Speaking negatively you might
    say, 'I can't help her, why should I? Skin would kill me if he knew
    I'd spoken to her'. Or, speaking positively, you might say 'My Dad
    would want me to help her but what can I possibly do?' You can
    talk to the students around you to discuss what the thoughts
    might be and rehearse what you are going to say. You must speak
    in the first person to narrate Luke's thoughts.

What have I learnt?

•   How does this activity help you to explore the tension and the
    layers of character that exist in the novel and play?

- Explain how this activity might help the actor prepare for the staging of other scenes in the play.
- What helped you to decide on Luke's thoughts?

Activity 8: Further exploration of the text

Learning outcomes

You will:

- develop the use of space, language, facial expression and gesture
- investigate and analyse the script, selecting relevant information to explore the significance of the star in the play
- analyse and question critically others' performances
- deduce and predict what events and themes are important in the play.

You will do this by analysing extracts from the play and making reasoned judgements about the information you are given.

1 You will be working in a group of three to five students. Each group has a different extract, as in Activity 5 (page 104), but this time, from different scenes in the play. Each group will also be given a simple musical instrument, such as a xylophone.

2 Produce a short **Digital Video Clip** of this extract. Begin with a **Still Image** followed by an **Action Reading** of the script and then freeze at the end. The **Still Images** at the beginning and end of the **Digital Video Clips** should be accompanied by note(s) produced on the instrument. Your group will need to think carefully about what atmosphere will be created by the note(s) you play at the beginning and the note(s) you play at the end. How might they change?

3 The extracts will be presented as **Rolling Theatre** but you will be using a slightly different technique by adding the musical notes at the beginning and end of your Clips. All the groups freeze in their

initial **Still Images**. The first group play their musical note(s), come to life, add the action and then freeze again, producing the sounds to accompany their final image. When they have frozen in their final image, the next group know that they can begin. This continues with each group producing their **Digital Video Clip** and punctuating their scenes with the **Still Images** and sounds until all the groups have shown their pieces.

Extracts

Extract 1: (lines 34–79, pages 14–16)

| *from* | MUM | What's happening to you? |
| *to* | MUM | … Or is it just because he isn't Dad? |

Extract 2: (lines 72–132, pages 20–22)

| *from* | MIRANDA | What happened to your face? |
| *to* | LUKE | What is it?' |

Extract 3: (lines 10–57, pages 23–25)

| *from* | HARDING | The isle is full of noises. |
| *to* | HARDING | The isle is full of noises. |

Extract 4: (stage instruction at start of Scene 5 to line 25, pages 25–27)

| *from* | | *A laptop computer glows invitingly…* |
| *to* | LUKE | … Why won't you speak to me? *(Pause)* Send. |

Extract 5: (lines 95–126, pages 32–34)

| *from* | SKIN | So? What happened? |
| *to* | SKIN | … And playing the piano. |

Extract 6: (line 1 to stage instruction at end of Scene 7, pages 36–38)

| *from* | LUKE | Miranda? |
| *to* | | … *she soon relaxes and plays the piece well.* |

Extract 7: (lines 18–62, pages 40–42)

from	MUM	I've never stopped loving your dad.
to	LUKE	I don't think so, Skin.

Extract 8: (lines 35–93, pages 45–47)

from	LITTLE	Natalie has a learning disability.
to	LITTLE	Anything. Anything you like.

Extract 9: (lines 36–87, pages 55–57)

from	LUKE	How do you know about the sounds I can hear?
to	MUM	Completely. It's just you and me now.

Extract 10: (lines 2–69, pages 61–63)

from	LUKE	I can hear sounds. Everywhere.
to	HARDING	… And the gateway to another world.

What have I learnt?

- What skills have you used/developed in this activity?
- What have you learnt about the significance of the star, sights and sounds? How does this relate to other ideas and events in *Starseeker*?
- How might the use of **Digital Video Clips** and music help your understanding of the writers' techniques.

Activity 9: Placing the text – unpacking the past

Learning outcomes

You will:

- write for a specific audience, with a specific purpose
- select appropriate information from the text
- explore the themes and tensions in the play
- organise and present your ideas appropriately.

You will do this by producing and placing pieces of text into the scene and making a contribution to the drama.

Placing the Text: participants create two identical paper copies of a text that could be found in a defined space in the drama. One copy is placed in the appropriate place; the other is retained by its authors. When a student/teacher in role picks up, points to or unfolds a placed text, the authors of that text read its contents out loud, providing an insight into a key character's world.

---

1   As a whole class, **sculpt** the scene in Mrs Little's bedroom described in Act Two, Scene 6 (stage instruction after line 38 to stage instruction after line 49, pages 66–67):

   from   *The effect of the music on Natalie is almost hypnotic.*

   to   *... he walks across to the box and opens it.*

2   **Sculpt** Luke into the scene at this point. Read on (stage instruction after line 49, page 67):

   He takes out a framed photograph and studies it. He puts the photograph down and takes out a letter.

3 Your teacher holds up a blank piece of paper in various positions within the scene while asking you what you think would be on the paper. Depending on where the piece of paper is positioned, you will make different suggestions as to what may be on it. If it is in the box, you might say it is a newspaper article about Barley. If it is in one of Luke's pockets or screwed up at his feet, you should suggest something different, such as a letter from Luke's father or a diary entry.

4 In pairs, create a piece of text that could appear in any of the places in the scene. It is important that you create two identical copies of this piece of text.

5 When you have all completed the pieces of text, set up the **sculpted** character again and in turn, place one copy of your text where you think it would be found in the scene. You need to remember where you placed your piece of text because you will be reading it out later when the character identifies it.

6 Once all the pieces of text have been placed, the **sculpted** character gradually comes to life. He turns to, looks at, and/or opens the pieces of text, one at a time. As he comes across each piece of text, he looks at it and freezes. If he has your piece of text at this point, you read it out loud from the identical copy you have written. You need to think about how you will read the text in terms of the tone, style and pace you might use.

7 The drama continues but stops at each piece of text while different students read them out, until all the pieces of text have been included. Music will be used to introduce and close the sequence.

8 When all the pieces of text have been read, Luke unfolds the original piece of paper and the teacher reads (lines 50–63, page 67):

from HUTCHINS   Dear Mrs Little, it is with regret...
to   HUTCHINS   ... Squadron Leader James P Hutchinson.

9 Move into a large circle. Your teacher will sit in the centre with the box and the objects laid out next to it on the floor. Your teacher will read (stage instruction after line 63 to line 64, page 67):

from		*Luke puts the letter on the table. He sees something else in the box – an identity bracelet.*
to	LUKE	*(reads from the bracelet)* 'Barley May Roberts.'

10 Your teacher will place all the objects in the box, move out of the circle and read (stage instruction after line 3 to line 18, pages 68–69):

from		*He opens his eyes and opens the laptop.*
to	LUKE	Natalie...

What have I learnt?

- What skills did you need to produce a piece of text that could be placed in the scene?
- What helped you to decide how to read out your piece of text?
- How might this activity help you to explore the tensions and themes of the play?
- What techniques has the playwright used to build up to these revelations?

Activity 10: Talking techniques

Learning outcomes

You will:

- investigate and analyse the playwright's techniques
- analyse and question the audience's response
- develop the use of space, language and movement.

You will do this by analysing extracts from the play and analysing the playwright's techniques and the audience's responses.

> **Talking Techniques:** Small groups **Action Read** extracts from a
> play, freezing the action at significant points to allow a student
> representing the playwright to reveal his/her intentions and a
> student representing the audience to reveal what they feel at
> that moment.

1   You will be working in a group of four to six students. Each group
    is given an extract from the play.

2   Choose who will take on the role of each character in the extracts.
    In addition, one person will represent the playwright and another
    person will represent the audience.

3   You will be producing an **Action Reading** of your extract but this
    time you will freeze the action at four significant points. To do this
    you will need to identify four key points where the playwright has
    used a specific technique to control the understanding and/or
    emotions of the audience.

    As the group **Action Reads** the extract, the playwright stands at
    one side of the action and the person representing the audience
    at the other side. When the action is frozen, the student
    representing the playwright will step forward and complete the
    phrase: 'As playwright, I have deliberately…'

    The student representing the audience will then step forward and
    respond by completing the phrase: 'As the audience, the effect on
    me is…'

4   Continue this process until the extract is complete, freezing the
    Action Reading four times and adding the playwright's and
    audience's comments.

Extracts

Extract 1: (stage instruction before line 24 to line 67, pages 50–51)

| from | | *The graveyard. Luke sits by his dad's headstone ...* |
| *to* | MIRANDA | I'm fine. |

Extract 2: (stage instruction at start of Scene 3 to line 35, pages 53–55)

| from | | *The kitchen. Mum is sitting at the table ...* |
| *to* | MUM | ... You even hear the same sounds. |

Extract 3: (lines 1–43, pages 58–60)

| *from* | NATALIE | Trees. |
| *to* | LUKE | ... An amazing five-pointed star. |

Extract 4: (stage instruction before line 13 to stage instruction after line 32, pages 64–65)

| *from* | | *Luke is walking over the bridge...* |
| *to* | | *Luke finishes gathering his sheet music and continues on his way to Mrs Little's house.* |

Extract 5: (stage instruction after line 20 to line 56, pages 69–70)

| *from* | | *Luke picks up the phone and dials...* |
| *to* | LUKE | Stop it, I'm trying to help! |

Extract 6: (lines 57–75, pages 70–71)

| *from* | MRS R | Are you still there? |
| *to* | MR R | Just tell us what we have to do. |

For example:

The actors **Action Read** the extracts, freezing at different points.

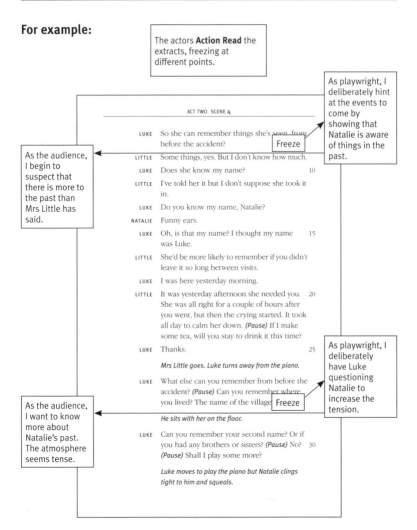

As playwright, I deliberately hint at the events to come by showing that Natalie is aware of things in the past.

As the audience, I begin to suspect that there is more to the past than Mrs Little has said.

ACT TWO SCENE 4

LUKE So she can remember things she's seen from before the accident? | Freeze

LITTLE Some things, yes. But I don't know how much.

LUKE Does she know my name? 10

LITTLE I've told her it but I don't suppose she took it in.

LUKE Do you know my name, Natalie?

NATALIE Funny ears.

LUKE Oh, is that my name? I thought my name 15 was Luke.

LITTLE She'd be more likely to remember if you didn't leave it so long between visits.

LUKE I was here yesterday morning.

LITTLE It was yesterday afternoon she needed you. 20 She was all right for a couple of hours after you went, but then the crying started. It took all day to calm her down. *(Pause)* If I make some tea, will you stay to drink it this time?

LUKE Thanks. 25

Mrs Little goes. Luke turns away from the piano.

LUKE What else can you remember from before the accident? *(Pause)* Can you remember where you lived? The name of the village | Freeze

He sits with her on the floor.

LUKE Can you remember your second name? Or if you had any brothers or sisters? *(Pause)* No? 30 *(Pause)* Shall I play some more?

Luke moves to play the piano but Natalie clings tight to him and squeals.

As playwright, I deliberately have Luke questioning Natalie to increase the tension.

As the audience, I want to know more about Natalie's past. The atmosphere seems tense.

What have I learnt?

• What skills have you used/developed in this activity?

• What have you learnt about the techniques the playwright has used and their effect on the audience?

• How might the use of this technique help you produce a written response to the play?

Activity 11: Exploring the adaptation process – from novel to script

Learning outcomes

You will:

- analyse the decisions and techniques used during the adaptation process
- select, organise and present relevant information and ideas in script and performance
- develop analytical skills and explore the writer's intentions
- consider the difficulties in staging a scene.

You will do this by analysing an extract from the novel and looking at how it might be adapted for the stage and the issues that might arise.

1   As a class, sit in a semi-circle facing the large projected text. Your teacher reads the following projected extract from Chapter 26 of the novel:

> Mrs Little's relief at the sight of him was obvious the moment she opened the front door [...]
> 'I'm taking you home, Barley,' he said.

2   The class is divided into groups of four or five. Each group is given the collective role of one of the following: playwright, novelist, director, teacher or Theatre Publicity Manager. In your groups, use the extract and the information you have gained from the work so far to say whether you feel the novel is suitable for adaptation. What aspects of the story do you think will be particularly successful and why? Do you foresee any difficulties? You will present these ideas to the Finance Director at a theatre.

3   The seating will be arranged to suggest the space where the meeting will take place.

4 The teacher in role as the Finance Director begins the meeting and explains the purpose of the gathering:

> 'Thank you for attending the meeting today. As you know, we are exploring the possibility of taking on a new adaptation of the novel *Starseeker* to be performed at the theatre next year. You will also be aware that the theatre is under great financial pressure at the moment. I need to be convinced that such a project would draw in large audiences and be able to cover its costs. It goes without saying that we also need to maintain the reputation of the theatre for staging high-quality productions.'

5 Using the **Meetings Convention**, contribute your ideas and arguments, including the evidence you have developed from the extract and the earlier work. Listen carefully to the views of others and decide how you can best present your case.

Meeting Convention: a group is gathered together in role to receive new information, agree actions or solve problems. The meeting may be chaired by a teacher or student in role, or may deliberately have no identified leader.

---

6 At the end of the meeting, your teacher in role as the Financial Director will close the discussion.

What have I learnt?

- What evidence and ideas did you use to help develop your argument?
- What did you feel were the most successful aspects of your argument? Why?
- How did this activity help you to understand the nature of the adaptation process and the issues and people involved?

Activity 12a: Placing the writer and the reader

Learning outcomes

You will:

- analyse authorial intention and techniques and explore the role of the reader and empathy in the text
- select and present evidence from the text to justify your comments
- listen with discrimination, weigh viewpoints and question critically.

You will do this by **Placing the Writer** and **Reader** into a particular scene in order to explore the intentions and techniques employed.

Placing the Author/Writer: in order to help students to appreciate an author's perspective, a student or teacher represents the presence, at a defined moment in the drama, of the author.

Placing the Audience/Reader: a similar process to **Placing the Author** but here a student or teacher represents the presence and/or perspective of the audience or reader at a defined moment in the drama.

---

1 Return to the extract from the novel below. Luke is intending to take Natalie away from Mrs Little's house.

> He carried her over to the window, both of them still humming, and stopped there for a moment, staring out over the garden towards the forest; then he turned back into the room. Mrs Little was still standing there, her face a mixture of relief and envy.

'You've obviously got the magic touch' [...] 'Because she's not yours,' he wanted to shout back at her. Because she's missing her parents and her friends. Because she can't see' [...] But all he said was: 'Mrs Little, could you make us something to drink?'

2   A student is given the role of Mrs Little. Using the space inside the circle, **sculpt** her into the position you believe she will be in when the action takes place. Think carefully about her facial expression. Other students may question this positioning and will re-sculpt Mrs Little into a position of their choosing.

3   Another student is given the role of Luke. The characters are **sculpted** into the scene and freeze while the following extract from the novel is read:

   from   'I expect Natalie could do with something and I certainly could.'

   to   'Anything'll do. Cup of tea, hot chocolate, whatever.'

4   Another member of the class is given the role of the 'writer' (Tim Bowler). Position the writer in the frozen scene where you think he should be. You might use various criteria for this, including the writer's distance from certain characters, the empathy created, the events, the writer's intention and what control the narrator has. Justify your choice, using evidence from the text to support your ideas. Discuss the positioning as a class. Throughout this discussion, other students should demonstrate the position they feel is most appropriate by moving and placing the writer and justifying their choice.

5   Another member of the class is given the role of the 'reader'. Position them in the frozen scene where you think they should be. You might use various criteria for this, including the reader's

distance from certain characters, the empathy felt, the events and the reader's understanding of a particular idea. Justify your choice, using evidence from the text to support your ideas. Discuss the positioning of the reader as a class. Throughout this discussion, other students should demonstrate the position they feel is most appropriate by moving and placing the reader and justifying their choice.

What have I learnt?

- How does physically **Placing the Writer** and/or **Reader** help your understanding of the writer's perspective and techniques?
- What skills were required when deciding where to place the reader or writer and justifying your choice?
- How did the discussion and repositioning inform your understanding/thinking?
- How was empathy created in this extract? Why?

Activity 12b: Placing the playwright

Learning outcomes

You will:

- analyse the adaptation process and discuss the complex decisions that are involved
- analyse the playwright's intention and techniques and explore the role of the audience in the play
- make decisions and select evidence to support your decisions and ideas.

You will do this by placing the playwright into the scene and exploring the techniques he has used and the decisions he has made.

1   Read the extract from the play of the same scene as the novel extract (Act Two, Scene 8, lines 1–20, pages 71–72):

from   LITTLE   I didn't expect you until late this afternoon...
to   LUKE   Anything will do. Cup of tea, hot chocolate, whatever.

2   As a whole class, return to the large circle. Using the space within the circle, **sculpt** the characters into the scene at this point in the play.

3   Discuss as a class the difficulties presented when taking the journey from script to stage. How would the director seeing the script for the first time know what is meant by Luke asking for a drink? How does the director know how Luke should ask the question, without having read and understood the novel? What does this say about the adaptation process? Is it the playwright or the director/actors who make the decisions about positioning, facial expressions and gestures? Does the playwright include many stage directions?

4   A member of the class is given the role of the 'playwright' (Phil Porter). Position him in the frozen scene where you think he should be. Justify your choice, using evidence from the text to support your ideas. Discuss the positioning as a class. Throughout the discussion, other students should demonstrate the position they feel is most appropriate by moving and placing the playwright and justifying their choice. Discuss whether this differs from the position of the writer in Activity 12a. Why? A student representing the 'audience' can now be placed in the same way and you can discuss the difference between placing the 'reader' and placing the 'audience'. Are there any differences? Discuss what this might tell us about the adaptation process.

What have I learnt?

- How does physically placing the playwright and audience help your understanding of the writer's perspective and techniques?
- How did this process develop your understanding of the adaptation process? What decisions do you feel the playwright had to make? Why?
- Are there aspects of the script that you would have done differently? Explain your comments by using evidence from the texts and referring to the activities that you have completed.

Activity 12c: Placing the director

Learning outcomes

You will:

- analyse the director's role in developing the play and discuss the complex decisions that are involved
- analyse the director's intention and techniques and explore the changes that are made
- make decisions and select evidence to support your decisions and ideas.

You will do this by placing the director into the scene and using **Communal Voice** to analyse the issues involved.

1   As a whole class, return to the **sculpted** images of Luke, Natalie and Mrs Little in Act Two, Scene 8.

2   A member of the class is given the role of the 'director' (Dani Parr – Director of the Northampton Royal & Derngate production). Position the director in the frozen scene where you think she should be. Justify your choice, using evidence from the text to support your ideas. Discuss the positioning as a class.

3 Read Dani Parr's comments about how she directed this scene:

In any play, I must consider as a director who our sympathies lie with, who our protagonist is. In this play, it is obviously Luke. In the adaptation process, Phil Porter and I made a very clear decision to make sure that the play, like the novel, reflected clearly the idea that this is Luke's journey. The challenge in translating this journey to the stage was to make sure that we felt at times like we could read Luke's mind, as we didn't have the benefit of the interior monologue that you get in the novel. In a way, this is a challenge for directors of any play, as it is crucial to understand the importance of subtext. The most important things in life are often not being said, they lie beneath the trivial things that we are talking about, and the fascinating thing about being a director is to try get to the bottom of what people really mean when they are saying something else. In this particular scene, when Luke asks for a drink, he obviously doesn't really want one. He is trying to make Mrs Little leave the room for long enough so that he can explain to Barley what is happening and physically carry her out of the house without being caught by Mrs Little. We need to see the tension in Luke and almost hear all the things that he wishes he could say to Mrs Little in the silences. We also need to believe that he is really scared but trying his best not to be. In this moment, we also concentrated on Eve Dallas (who played Mrs Little) heightening her air of suspicion. She senses something is up with Luke and as an audience, I wanted us to think that she might catch him out at any point, and like the scene when he is looking into the box earlier on, this adds to our tension and makes the play feel like more of a thriller, which was always our aim. We made sure that whenever Luke and Mrs Little were talking to each other in any scene, there was the feeling that they were asking 'Can I trust you? Who are you really? What do you know?', whatever they were actually saying. We also wanted there to be a feeling of mutual need from both of them so that we felt we understood why they didn't just give up on this difficult relationship.

In terms of blocking this particular scene, we felt that Barley should be physically near the piano as much as possible, and we removed the front panel of the piano so that she could crawl into the space where the piano stool would normally be, and her cries then resonated into the piano and the strings, giving her voice an eerie quality. The piano was downstage and so when Luke came into the room, he physically pulled her to him on the floor and held her to him, whilst humming 'Reverie' to her, a symbol of her old life. This presented a picture which clearly outlined where sympathies should lie: Mrs Little hovering upstage centre by the door deciding whether to leave her with him or not. When she left, Michael Moore who played Luke ran to the door to check she really had gone to the kitchen and then picked Barley up and left really quickly. The speed of this section really contrasted with the slow tension of the temporary stand-off between Luke and Mrs Little. I think the way that Eve, Michael and Tamsin played this scene showed clearly the mix of emotions: the relief from Mrs Little that the crying has stopped, but the jealousy of being shut out of this little unit. Tamsin would show how much Barley needed Luke by really clinging to him like she was drowning and would clearly show that she trusted him enough to not be upset when he took her out of the house.

4 Does your positioning of the director now change? Why?

What have I learnt?

- How does physically placing the director and playwright help your understanding of the writing and performance processes?
- How did this process develop your understanding of the

adaptation process? What decisions do you feel the playwright and/or director had to make? Why?

- Are there any other aspects of the script that you would have done differently? Explain your comments by using evidence from the texts and by referring to the activities that you have completed.

Activity 12d: Does the writer have a role in the script and performance?

Learning outcomes

You will:

- use your understanding of the adaptation process of *Starseeker* to think critically about the role of the writers in other adaptations
- analyse the relationship between writer, scriptwriter and director and the differences/similarities between the role of the reader and that of the audience
- make decisions and select evidence to support your decisions and ideas.

You will do this by considering the role of Tim Bowler, the original writer of the novel, in the adapted version of *Starseeker*, and questioning the significance of this to the general process of adaptation.

1   Return to the sculpted scene from Activities 12b and 12c, which includes the playwright, the director and the audience. The student who represented the 'writer' (Tim Bowler) earlier (in Activity 12a), should stand at the side of the frozen scene. Should Tim Bowler be placed into the sculpted scene and, if so, where? Does the original writer remain part of the text? Are they left outside the scene? Are they near to the playwright or director, or do they have a different perspective? Position the 'writer' where you feel it is most appropriate for them to be.

2 Discuss the positioning as a class. Throughout the discussion, other students should demonstrate the position they feel is most appropriate by moving and placing the 'writer' and justifying their choices. Discuss what this might tell us about the adaptation process. Would this be the case with all adaptations?

What have I learnt?

- How have Activities 12a/b/c/d helped your understanding of this particular scene and the adaptation process?
- What might the actors or director gain from taking part in similar activities?
- Who did you find most difficult to position? Why? What skills and understanding were required for this?

Activity 13: Characters' ghosts

Learning outcomes

You will:

- investigate and analyse the text to identify what influences the characters' thoughts and motivation
- explore the tensions in the play
- organise and present your ideas.

You will do this by creating a scene to reveal a character's 'ghost' and to question what inspires and haunts them.

1 Your teacher will explain that one of the techniques the playwright has used in adapting the novel has been the introduction of Luke's dad's ghost. You will be working in a group of three to five students to present the particular scenes where the ghost is included. Each group is given an extract.

Extract 1: Act One, Scene 5 *Quite suddenly somewhere else in the house, someone begins to play... Luke slams the piano shut* (page 27)

Extract 2: Act One, Scene 7 *The humming sound returns. Luke approaches a gravestone... The sounds fade away* (pages 35–36)

Extract 3: Act Two, Scene 2 *Luke's bedroom. He is exhausted... Dad is plunged into darkness. Pause* (pages 52–53)

Extract 4: Act Two, Scene 10 *Luke sits at the piano... he is Luke's imagination* (pages 83–84)

Extract 5: Act Two, Scene 11 *Luke turns to look at the tree...* Dad?! (page 88)

2 In your group, produce a **Digital Video Clip** of the extract and, as a class, produce your **Digital Video Clips** as **Rolling Theatre** (see Activity 5, pages 104–105).

3 Discuss the purpose of adding these scenes to the play. In what ways does Luke's dad both inspire and haunt him?

4 Working in the same groups, your teacher will give you a character, together with short extracts relating to them. Discuss what haunts and inspires your character. Produce a short **Digital Video Clip**, similar to the ones that include Luke's dad to show the character's own 'ghost'. (See further instructions for this technique on page 134.)

Extracts

Roger
Extract 1: (lines 15–22, page 13)

| *from* | ROGER | You're late back... |
| *to* | ROGER | Of you, I— |

Extract 2: (lines 36–45, page 83)

| *from* | MUM | That was Roger. He got your message.... |
| *to* | LUKE | I always said he was a nice bloke. |

Miranda

Extract 1: (lines 84–109, pages 20–21)

| *from* | MIRANDA | Can you help me with something? |
| *to* | LUKE | No problem. |

Extract 2: (lines 114–118, page 21)

| *from* | MIRANDA | That would be great... |
| *to* | MIRANDA | ... Instead of all this other stuff. |

Extract 3: (lines 5–26, pages 86–87)

| *from* | MIRANDA | Luke, where are you going? |
| *to* | LUKE | Sorry. |

Extract 4: (lines 35–41, pages 88–89)

| *from* | MIRANDA | Luke? Are you all right? |
| *to* | LUKE | I know. |

Mr Harding

Extract 1: (lines 10–21, pages 23–24)

| *from* | HARDING | The isle is full of noises. |
| *to* | HARDING | ... Let it help you— |

Extract 2: (lines 9–28, page 61)

| *from* | LUKE | Mum told me Dad heard the same things. |
| *to* | HARDING | ... You hear the sounds, I never will. |

Mrs Little

Extract 1: (lines 49–73, pages 45–46)

| *from* | LITTLE | Ever since the crash... |
| *to* | LITTLE | I don't. |

Extract 2: (lines 84–91, page 47)

| *from* | LUKE | Why have you got a piano... |
| *to* | LITTLE | ... For my granddaughter. |

Extract 3: (lines 21–39, page 85)

from	LITTLE	All I ever wanted, apart from Bill...
to	LITTLE	... I was meant to find her.

Mum
Extract 1: (lines 18–41, pages 40–41)

from	MUM	I've never stopped loving your dad.
to	MUM	... If that's what made me happy.

Extract 2: (lines 32–55, pages 55–56)

from	MUM	Your dad used to do that.
to	MUM	... he thought they might leave him.

Natalie
Extract 1: (stage instruction after line 33 to line 43, pages 59–60)

from		*Natalie hums the first six notes of 'Rêverie'...*
to	LUKE	... An amazing five-pointed star.

Extract 2: (lines 56–70, page 74)

from	LUKE	Are you all right?
to	LUKE	... And they're going to look after you again.

Daz
Extract 1: (lines 13–22, pages 64–65)

from	DAZ	See. I told you he wouldn't be here.
to	SKIN	He's like a little worm. He keeps slipping through my fingers—

Extract 2: (lines 103–118, pages 76–77)

from	DAZ	I reckon he's learnt his lesson
to	DAZ	But do we have to?

Extract 3: (lines 46–48, page 83)

| *from* | LUKE | Who called the ambulance? |
| *to* | MUM | ... an attack of conscience. |

Barley's parents
Extract 1: (lines 6–20, pages 68–69)

| *from* | MRS R | We haven't seen our beautiful daughter... |
| *to* | MRS R | ... call the number below. |

Extract 2: (lines 59–74, pages 70–71)

| *from* | MRS R | You have to understand... |
| *to* | MRS R | 'Rêverie'. |

5 Instead of presenting the extracts as **Rolling Theatre**, you will use a slightly different technique. All the groups freeze in the initial **Still Images**. The first group come to life, add the action and then freeze again. When they have frozen in their final image, the character whose ghost is being presented steps out of the **Still Image** (as if someone has clicked on a **hypertext** on a screen to find out more information). They step forward and explain what the ghost is and what haunts and inspires them. They then step back into the **Still Image** and the next group know that they can begin. This continues with all the groups producing their **Digital Video Clip** and spoken **hypertext** until all groups have shown their pieces.

Ghosts Hypertext: This convention, inspired by hotlinks on a website, deliberately interrupts a narrative to provide hidden information such as an insight into a character's motivations. While a small group drama is taking place, the action is frozen to allow one of the characters in the group to step out of the scene and describe to an audience how another character or situation in their drama *haunts* or *inspires* them.

---

6   The students who were in role as ghosts move into a circle in the middle of the room, as they are about to hold a ghosts' counsel. The rest of the class forms a larger circle around them.

7   The teacher asks the ghosts to discuss with each other how they haunt and inspire the people they are connected to. Their task is to discover what similarities and differences they have. The rest of the class listen carefully to the ghosts' counsel and think about how the ideas have been integrated into the script.

What have I learnt?

- How does this activity help you to explore the tension and the characters in the play?
- Explain how such an activity might help the actors prepare for the staging of the play.
- What skills did you use during the group activity and what helped you to decide on what haunts and inspires each character?

Activity 14: Choosing life

Learning outcomes

You will:

- make reasoned judgements and organise and present your ideas
- investigate and analyse the text to identify the characters' thoughts and motivation
- continue to explore and analyse the tension in the play.

You will do this by creating the 'Voices of Reason' in Luke's head, which enable him to make a decision.

Voices of Reason: an expanded version of the convention **Conscience Alley,** where collectively students create a reasoned argument by interrupting a text to inform a character's decision.

1   As a class, sit in a semi-circle facing the large projected text. Your teacher reads the following projected extract from the play (Act Two, Scene 8, lines 163–181, pages 80–81):

> I'm falling.
> But at the same time going up...
> And I think of Dad.

2   You will be working in a group of three to four students. Your teacher will allocate the name of one character, mentioned in this speech, to your group, which you are going to focus on. Drawing on your knowledge of the character's relationship with Luke in the play, develop the speech that Luke might hear to help him decide whether to choose life. You need to decide who will say what and how the speech is said.

3   The teacher will adopt the role of Luke and stand in the middle of the room with the identified character groups around her/him. The teacher reads the extract again:

> I think of Mum
> And Miranda...

The teacher will pause at the end of each line, allowing the group representing that character to say its speech. This will continue until all the characters in the extract have spoken.

4   The teacher concludes the activity by reading the next line:

> I'm ready to live.

What have I learnt?

- How does this activity help you to explore the tension and the different layers of character that exist in the play?
- Explain how such an activity might help the actor prepare for the staging of this scene in the play.
- What helped you to decide on the character's reasoning?

Activity 15: Dramatic Hypertexts – creating a physical website

Before you prepare for the final activities, look back at the headings of all the activities you have done so far. This would also be a good opportunity to discuss all the ideas, comments and quotations collected on the colour spectrum, throughout the work.

Learning outcomes

You will:

- explore the links that are established throughout the play
- use the understanding you have gained from all the other activities to approach the last activity critically and with integrity
- consider what synaesthesia is and how it affects Luke
- demonstrate an understanding of the drama process.

You will do this by producing a physical website that could be used to accompany a production of the play.

Dramatic Hypertexts: This convention, inspired by hotlinks on a website, allows groups of participants to represent dramatically the information gathered on a website to support their understanding of a text or production of a play. Small groups produce a physical representation of a webpage. One group is the main page or *homepage* and the other groups are the hypertexts or *webpages* that are linked to the homepage. Each of the webpages can be activated when triggered by the group representing the *homepage*.

---

1 As a class, discuss how emails and websites have been used as theatrical devices throughout the play. Your teacher will show you some pages from the National Theatre website that was used to support a production of the play *Coram Boy*. As a class, you are aiming to produce a physical representation of a website like this to support a production of *Starseeker*.

2 Groups of three or four students will each be given a page of the website to work on. One group will be given the main page and each other group will have a page that is linked to the main page through a specific hypertext. These might include 'Adapting the play', 'Staging the play', 'Key themes and ideas', and 'Key scenes'. Each 'hypertext' group will be given its hypertext title on a large piece of paper. If you have not already explored what synaesthesia is, your teacher will explain its meaning.

3 Produce a physical representation of your webpage. You will need to think carefully about what dramatic techniques you might use to provide different aspects of the page, such as text, **Still Images**, interviews, discussions and extracts from the performance. The glossary at the back of the book might help you to do this.

4 Select a coloured ribbon that best represents the link between the main page and the page you are working on.

5 The group who have been allocated the main page place themselves in the middle of the room. This 'main page' group will, within the space they are using, have all the hypertext titles and ribbons collected in from the other groups. All the other 'hypertext' groups will be positioned around the 'main page' group. These 'hypertext' groups need to freeze in the **Still Image** that would be seen when first visiting their page.

6   The 'main page' group in the centre comes to life and presents the physical representation of the homepage. At appropriate points, when a hypertext title is mentioned, someone from the 'main page' group picks up one end of the ribbon and takes it to the relevant 'hypertext' group. This 'hypertext' group then brings its page to life. When they have finished, the ribbon is taken back to the 'main page'. This continues until all aspects of the production website are covered. At the end all the groups freeze in their initial images.

What have I learnt?

- How has this activity helped you to develop your understanding of the play?
- What benefit might the actors or directors gain from taking part in such activities?
- How might this work help you with your written responses to the play?

Activity 16: How music and images bring together the beginning and end of the play

Learning outcomes

You will:

- explore the links made between the beginning and end of the play
- analyse the significance of the journeys the characters have made throughout the play
- use your understanding gained from all the other activities to approach the ending of the play critically and with integrity
- consider the significance of sound and sight in the play
- demonstrate an understanding of the drama process.

1   Everyone in the class is seated in a large semi-circle facing the projected text of an extract from the beginning of the play, and has with them the word they were given at the beginning of the work on the play (see Activity 1, page 96).

2   The class will read out all the words around the circle, thinking carefully about what they now mean. The teacher then reads the end of the play (Act Two, Scene 11, lines 60–65, page 90):

HARDING: So without further ado, it's with no small measure of pride that I give to you Luke Stanton playing a piece by...?

LUKE: Stanton.

HARDING: Stanton, and which Stanton is that?

LUKE: Both.

Luke plays the previously unfinished piece that he composed with his dad in Act Two, Scene 10.

3   The music used in Activity 1 is played again (the music composed by Luke and his father).

4   You will be working in the same groups that you were in for Activity 1. In your groups, reproduce the **Still Image** that you created at the start of the work in response to the text and music, selecting and placing the ribbon again.

5   Now create a **Still Image** that defines your current response to the text and music. Would you use the same colour ribbon or introduce a new one? Write down on a large sheet of paper a significant word or phrase from the work you have been doing. It can be taken from the script or it might be a response or idea that was developed from the activities. Place it in front of your **Still Image**. Consider how the words or phrase might be said while holding the second **Still Image**. What tone or volume might you use?

6 All the groups will hold their first **Still Image**. The first group will
   then gradually merge from this into their second **Still Image**. As
   they do so, they move or add the ribbons as appropriate, and
   speak the word or phrase. Once they have finished, the next
   group will know they can begin; holding the first image for a few
   seconds, merging into the second image and speaking the words.
   This process will continue until all the groups have merged from
   one image to the other. The music is played throughout.

What have I learnt?

- How has the final activity helped you to develop your
  understanding of the end of the play?
- What journeys have the characters gone on throughout the play?
- What do the two **Still Images** tell you about the journey you have
  gone on?

Reflecting on all the activities

- Which skills have you developed or learned through this work?
  How will your teacher be able to tell you have learned or
  developed these skills?
- Which activity do you think helped you most to enjoy, understand
  and/or analyse the play? Why?
- Choose two other scenes from the play and think about which
  drama activities or conventions you could use to explore these
  scenes. Explain why you would use those particular activities and
  what you would be expecting people to learn from them.
- Choose two of the activities, either from above, or that you have
  devised, that you feel a director about to stage the play should
  use with the actors. Explain your choice and justify why you think
  it would benefit those involved in a performance of *Starseeker*.

Glossary

Action Reading students, in role, walk through a scene, speaking lines and adding gestures and movements, while reading from scripts

Communal Voice individual members of the group take up positions, one at a time, behind a sculpted character and speak the words that the character says at a chosen moment in the drama

Conscience Alley the group is divided into two lines facing each other. A student (or teacher) in role as a character in the drama walks between the two lines as individuals speak out what is in the character's conscience. Each line might represent opposing perspectives

Digital Video Clip a short, repeatable dramatic sequence is 'bookended' with a **Still Image** at the start and a **Still Image** at the end

Dramatic Hypertexts This convention, inspired by hotlinks on a website, allows groups of participants to represent dramatically the information gathered on a website to support their understanding of a text or production of a play. Small groups produce a physical representation of a webpage. One group is the main page or *homepage* and the other groups are the hypertexts or *webpages* that are linked to the homepage. Each of the webpages can be activated when triggered by the group representing the *homepage*

Ghosts Hypertext This convention, inspired by hotlinks on a website, deliberately interrupts a narrative to provide hidden information such as an insight into a character's motivations. While a small group drama is taking place, the action is frozen to allow one of the characters in the group to step out of the scene and describe to an audience how another character or situation in their drama *haunts* or *inspires* them

Guided Tour in pairs, A (with eyes open) leads B (with eyes closed) slowly through an imaginary environment while providing a spoken commentary. The environment or location may be based on text but will usually be stimulated by a printed or projected map or 'bird's-eye' picture. Roles can be reversed to enable all participants to share the experience

Meeting Convention a group is gathered together in role to receive new information, agree actions or solve problems. The meeting may be chaired by a teacher or student in role, or may deliberately have no identified leader

Placing the Audience/Reader a similar process to **Placing the Author** but here a student or teacher represents the presence and/or perspective of the audience or reader at a defined moment in the drama

Placing the Author/Writer in order to help students to appreciate an author's perspective, a student or teacher represents the presence, at a defined moment in the drama, of the author

Placing the Text participants create two identical paper copies of a text that could be found in a defined space in the drama. One copy is placed in the appropriate place; the other is retained by its authors. When a student/teacher in role picks up, points to or unfolds a placed text, the authors of that text read its contents out loud, providing an insight into a key character's world

Role on the Spectrum to help define character traits at particular moments in drama, a colour spectrum is placed in front of the participants. Students place words about a character onto the colour spectrum, thinking carefully about the colour on which they place each word

Rolling Theatre groups can share their work on different aspects of a drama, learning from each other by running several rehearsed sections in a sequence

Sculpting participants offer suggestions while placing an individual in a significant, frozen position so that considered analysis can take place

Spectactor performers in a drama session can follow the action with their eyes and heads when the focus is not directly upon them

Still Image a Still Image is created by participants in the drama standing motionless, often at a given sign by the teacher or as a result of being **sculpted** by other students into the frozen image. This convention is used to mark a significant moment or enable time for reflection

Talking Techniques Small groups **Action Read** extracts from a play, freezing the action at significant points to allow a student representing the playwright to reveal his/her intentions and a student representing the audience to reveal what they feel at that moment

Voices of Reason an expanded version of the convention **Conscience Alley**, where collectively students create a reasoned argument by interrupting a text to inform a character's decision